Love
&
Health

Twelve Primary Ingredients,
Showing how to Balance Your
Physical, Mental and Spiritual Well-Being.

Jerry L. Ainsworth, Ed.D., MPH

PeaceMakers
Publishing
in cooperation with

PUBLISHING

Note for Librarians: A cataloguing record for this book is available from Library and Archives
Canada at www.collectionscanada.ca/amicus/index-e.html
ISBN 1-4120-9566-2

Printed on paper with minimum 30% recycled fibre.
Trafford's print shop runs on "green energy" from solar, wind and other environmentally-friendly power sources.

PeaceMakers
Publishing
in cooperation with

Offices in Canada, USA, Ireland and UK

Book sales for North America and international:
Trafford Publishing, 6E–2333 Government St.,
Victoria, BC V8T 4P4 CANADA
phone 250 383 6864 (toll-free 1 888 232 4444)
fax 250 383 6804; email to orders@trafford.com
Book sales in Europe:
Trafford Publishing (UK) Limited, 9 Park End Street, 2nd Floor
Oxford, UK OX1 1HH UNITED KINGDOM
phone +44 (0)1865 722 113 (local rate 0845 230 9601)
facsimile +44 (0)1865 722 868; info.uk@trafford.com
Order online at:
trafford.com/06-1321

10 9 8 7 6 5 4

To My Parents,
Fern and Ottis Ainsworth,
who loved me.

Contents

Preface

This book is the story of a college course on love and health that I gave for twenty-four years at Southern Connecticut State University and of the efforts to implement its principles at Griffin Health Services, a local hospital.

While teaching, I followed what Leo Buscaglia taught me: "Sit with your students and have a conversation." As a result, student-initiated questions took our class discussions in many different explorative directions. Yet, somehow, we not only covered all the material the course outline required but also learned to utilize practical applications of love and health in our personal lives.

While coordinating my service as hospital chaplain with Griffin's innovative administrative programs, we witnessed countless miracles of healing, comfort, and change of attitude among patients as we actualized the therapeutic power of love. Griffin became a healing environment that drew the attention of many hospitals around the world and from which many people sought inspiration.

This book sets out the guidelines we used to further our understanding of the relationship between love and health.

Jerry L. Ainsworth
October 2004

1

Beginnings

In 2003, I retired from Southern Connecticut State University, where I had worked in a variety of capacities for over thirty years. At this school, I had moved rapidly up the ladder of success—from associate professor to full professor to program coordinator to department chairman to director of the largest division on campus. I regarded such progress as quite an accomplishment, considering what my background had been.

As a boy, I knew I was loved but felt more part of a collective process. I didn't know what my purpose in life was, only that I proved difficult to handle. The notion of positive self-esteem was never a part of my world view. Growing up on a farm in Louisiana provided endless opportunities for getting into trouble. My fun regularly turned into fear as I contemplated a nightly reckoning with my father after a daily excess of mischievous deeds.

When my mother introduced me as, "My son Jerry—my argument for birth control," I was led to believe there was something wrong with me. I was made to feel the least desirable of the five children of our otherwise peaceful home.

In contrast, my two older brothers were bright students and excellent athletes. The perception of a "dumb little brother" came easily to them. Everyone in the family seemed to reflect that opinion. This view of myself unfortunately affected my perception of love and well-being and I fully accepted it for the first twenty years of my life.

Several events, however, changed my feelings of worthlessness to one of self-worth. The first was the two years I served as a voluntary missionary for my church in a foreign land. Amidst all the challenges, I realized I had grit. I was *not* dumb but as capable as anyone else in fulfilling my task. Leadership skills surfaced that I had experienced as captain of my college gymnastics team but that now translated into real life.

The second was an IQ test, a requirement for a college psychology course. Believing I would score lowest in the class, I put it off to the very last. Even when the results came back I couldn't bring myself to look at them and discover the embarrassing report. After weeks of internal torment, I opened the envelope, stunned to find the opposite of what I had expected—someone must have made a mistake!

With a growing assurance that I was, in fact, capable and intelligent, I continued in college and finally completed a doctorate in Education. I joined the faculty at Southern Connecticut State University, where I quickly gained a reputation as a good teacher. I felt I had learned how to survive, indeed succeed, in the political arena of higher education. My life, which had been tempestuous in the past, now looked promising.

With an additional degree in Public Health from Yale Medical School, and a year as visiting scholar at Yale Law School, I had developed excellent post-doctoral credentials and soon found myself a fully tenured professor heading up the largest division at the university. Any lingering doubts that I was dumb were forever dispelled, or so I thought.

While administering my division, I had developed warm relationships with many colleagues. I had created new and exciting programs, college courses, and new departments, hiring new professors to fill their positions. With these positive developments, I was surely destined for a life of success.

Yet, when I was informed the vice-president of the university wanted to see me, I had that same feeling in my stomach as at age seven when my father would call me to account for my misdeeds. There was a part of me that, when confronted with persons in authority, expected to be disciplined, scolded, and punished. It wasn't clear to me why I felt that way. Nor was it clear why I felt *compelled* to move up the administrative ladder and assume such important roles in the first place. Why was I working so hard to become a vice-president and, ultimately, of course, a college president?

Still, I would become what people told me I should become. Besides, I was making a decent living doing what I enjoyed. I had a large circle of friends. Indeed, I would go so far as to say I was revered as a pretty savvy character, a true leader, one who could straighten out a bureaucracy, swim against the tide, and not be corrupted by the system. All saw that I was a person of integrity and principle who could make an academic institution work right—a true Sir Galahad in a den of political dragons. I was certain the system would never "get me" as many had warned.

Impressive degrees hung in my office. I was one of the youngest full professors and administrators on campus and was consistently proving that I was good at what I did. My rapid promotions proved it. That is what I thought and felt at the time. Not only was I an esteemed member of the Round Table, I would show everyone that right could prevail.

I was determined to continue building the academic legacy I had so admirably created at my university. I would conquer all challenges and proceed up the ladder. I would prove to my siblings that I was not dumb. My parents would realize it was a good thing that I was born. Though I didn't realize it at the time, these were the underlying motives behind my behavior; that was what was driving me.

As a person of influence, I could virtually dictate the outcomes of campus debates in my favor. But such political power quickly brought me into conflict with the new president. He decided to change the focus of the university from teacher training to a more liberal arts philosophy. To my mind, here was an opportunity for Sir Galahad, the dragon slayer, to pit himself against the evil administration. Here was my chance to valiantly represent my seventy-two-member faculty who looked to me as their general and protagonist. I was in search of academia's Holy Grail and ardently believed I would find it.

Of course, the politically smart thing to do would be to give in to the administration, make it look as if I had fought a good fight, but in the end give the institution what it wanted. However, Sir Galahad would never do that.

The quarrel I had with the administration lasted more than a year. After many contentious and heated disagreements, I ended up in a debate with the vice-president in front of a group of faculty. A few days after that exchange, I received a letter from him firing me from my post and demoting me to the position of a regular faculty member.

I was floored. I had become division director through the faculty's own recommendation. I expected them now to vote again and recommend that I retain the directorship and continue the battle I had been waging in their behalf. They didn't.

What a shock that was to me, and what a horrendous disappointment! I believed they would fight for me with the same ferocity I had fought for them. How wrong I was! I had just learned my first lesson in the political realities of bureaucratic survival: the pack eventually turns on its leader.

I suddenly went from being a prince on campus to a pariah. Faculty members saw what could happen to a person who bucked the system, and they weren't about to risk incurring the wrath of the administration that had been unleashed on me. With their personal survival in mind, the same faculty members with whom I had lunched on a regular basis now avoided being seen with me altogether. Of the seventy-two in my division, only two were willing to be viewed as my close friends.

Forget the beautiful principles I had taught, indeed had practiced! My Camelot had become a myth. People were right: the system would ultimately prevail. It simply wasn't possible to be a person of principle in a bureaucratic setting. It was easy for me then to conclude that I had not, in fact, learned to survive. The feeling I had was the same as the one I experienced years earlier when family members dismissed me as dumb. This time however, I believed I was right.

I was hurt, demoralized, and angry. I cleared out my office a month early, hung Rudyard Kipling's poem, "If," on my office door, and left for Mexico. As it was the end of the school year, I did what I usually did and spent the summer months south of the border. There, however, I allowed my anger to fester.

IF

If you can keep your head when all about you
Are losing theirs and blaming it on you,
If you can trust yourself when all men doubt you,
But make allowance for their doubting too;
If you can wait and not be tired by waiting,
Or being lied about, don't deal in lies,
Or being hated, don't give way to hating,
And yet don't look too good, nor talk too wise;

If you can dream – and not make dreams your master;
If you can think – and not make thoughts your aim;
If you can meet with Triumph and Disaster
And treat those two imposters just the same;
If you can bear to hear the truth you've spoken
Twisted by knaves to make a trap for fools,
Or watch the things you gave your life to, broken,
And stoop and build 'em up with worn-out tools:

If you can make one heap of all your winnings
And risk it on one turn of pitch and toss,
And lose, and start again at your beginnings
And never breathe a word about your loss;
If you can force your heart and nerve and sinew
To serve your turn long after they are gone,
And so hold on when there is nothing in you
Except the Will which says to them: "Hold on!"

If you can talk with crowds and keep your virtue,
Or walk with Kings – nor lose the common touch,
If neither foes nor loving friends can hurt you,
If all men count with you, but none too much;
If you can fill the unforgiving minute
With sixty seconds' worth of distance run,
Yours is the Earth and everything that's in it,
And – which is more – you'll be a Man, my son!

Rudyard Kipling

On my return in the Fall, the precious poem had been ripped from the door, my name had been removed from all division notices, and my locker in the dressing room had been emptied and given to another. Not only had I been fired, I had been erased.

As a person of integrity, who adhered to ideal principles, I felt double-crossed and abandoned. Waves of anger welled up in me. My response was anything but ideal—it was visceral: I decided to get even.

Though I knew how to apply correct principles, I had not been required to do so when hurt, depressed, and rejected. I had used those principles only when things went well. I had never transferred them from my mind to my heart. They were a part of my brain, not my being. It would be years before I could appreciate the sentiment of these words by Henry Ward Beecher: "It is trial that proves one thing weak and another strong. A house built on the sand is, in fair weather, just as good as if built on a rock. A cobweb is as the mightiest cable when there is no strain on it."

In my brooding anger, I allied myself with those who regarded themselves enemies of the administration. For me, this would be an all-out war. I did everything I could to cause pain and discomfort to those who had wronged me. I resolved to be as cold and mean-spirited as I assumed they were. By so doing, I believed I could win.

I participated in those petty campus squabbles no one takes seriously but their participants. Common bureaucrats had gotten in my way, interrupting my ascent up the ladder. They had impeded my progress towards becoming a college president, a position for which I believed I was destined. They had prevented me from obtaining the Holy Grail. I was therefore determined with an unholy zeal to heap on them my self-righteous indignation. And while thus engaged, I would additionally punish them, although unknowingly, for all the vexations and embarrassments of my childhood.

In reality, as I look back, that unhappy experience taught me a valuable lesson about who I was and who I wasn't. It taught me what I *should* become, in contrast to what I and others *thought* I should become. I learned a fundamental principle, namely that there are two ways to learn something, either through love or through pain. As far too many people do today, I was learning through pain. One sage expressed it well: "Those who will not hear must feel."

While acting out my virulent anger towards the administration, I woke up one morning and passed blood. I visited my physician. After a battery of tests and some intense questioning, he said, "You have an intestinal problem that, in my opinion, is caused by anger. I recommend one of three courses of action: either change your job, change your girlfriend, or pick six friends to be your pallbearers because if you don't you're probably going to die." What a shocker! But on reflection I suspected he was right.

As my training was in research, I decided to check out the literature to see if anger could kill people. I knew it was unhealthy, but I had never considered it might kill, especially me. I plowed through the literature. Sure enough, uncontrolled anger was as lethal as any ingested toxin, perhaps more so.

I quickly decided my enemies were not worth dying over. So I released the pent-up feelings I had towards those who had fired me and towards my colleagues who had refused to stand by me—I let it all go. To my surprise, that proved much easier than I had anticipated, especially given the alternative.

Having done this, I was irresistibly drawn back to the literature I had just researched. Not only did I discover the harmful effects of uncontrolled anger, I also found a plethora of data indicating the healthy effects of positive emotions. The literature was abundant and overpowering. I was deeply chagrined that I, a seasoned health educator, had not appreciated that before. I had finally learned what Marcus Aurelius had written over eighteen hundred years earlier: "How much more grievous are the consequences of anger than the causes of it."

Then and there, I decided I would write a course on Love and Health. Because I had written and won approval for many academic courses in the past, I assumed this would be an easy task.

LOVE AND FIRE

Someday, after we have mastered the air, the winds, the tides, and gravity, we will harness for God the energies of love. And then, for the second time in the history of the world, man will have discovered fire.

Teilhard de Chardin

2

Love is like the sun. It warms and encompasses everything but restricts nothing
—Santayana

A Course on Love and Health

As with previous new courses, I looked around for what other universities might be teaching on this topic. I waded through countless college catalogues. To my astonishment, I could find no college course whose primary focus related love to health. I was appalled to discover no mention of this intrinsic human experience in all of academia, let alone a fully developed course demonstrating how love, or the lack of love, influences a person's well-being.

I had heard, however, that Leo Buscaglia taught a course on love at a university in California so I called him and requested a copy of his syllabus. He laughed, "Jerry, we don't have one. We just sit and talk about love."

I understood, of course, that such an unprofound approach would never pass muster with my university's curriculum committee. I realized I would have to start from scratch. So I pulled out all the supporting data from the literature, organized the material in a systematic way, and wrote a proposal that I felt made an excellent case for a college course on Love and Health.

I had been before the curriculum committee many times in the past, so I knew they took fresh proposals seriously. Still, I was unprepared for the negative reactions they responded with. These were some of their replies:

- This sounds like nothing but a bunch of fluff.
- Ainsworth has no credentials for teaching this topic.
- This subject doesn't belong in health but in psychology.
- What does he know about love? He's not even married.
- Such a course will mess up the minds of those who take it.
- There's no worthy body of research to support this proposal.
- Even if he gives the course, no one will take it seriously.
- It will definitely die from a lack of enrollment.

Though I made what I felt was a good case for Love and Health, I was disappointed to find that this reflected their final decision. To make a long story short, I rewrote the course many times during the next two years before finally winning approval. Surprisingly, most opposed to it on campus was the Nursing Department. In fact, even after the course won approval from the curriculum committee, the Nursing Department continued to vote against it. I wondered, sometimes out loud, "What has the nursing profession got against love and health?"

Although gaining approval had been a big initial obstacle, teaching Love and Health proved to be an even greater one. In our first semester, for example, I could find no book I could seriously consider appropriate as a text. That was years before Bernie Siegel's book, *Love, Medicine, and Miracles* appeared. Nowadays, a person can choose from any number of such publications, many of which make excellent textbooks.

Moreover, as I began teaching Love and Health, the first mistake I made was to assume I understood love. I quickly discovered that I, the teacher, had many things to learn myself about this subject. The curriculum committee's words often reverberated in my ears: "What does he know about love? He's not even married." In fact, as the course developed year after year, and as it became more streamlined and refined, I know that I ended up learning far more about love than any of my students.

A second mistake I made was to assume that everyone had experienced family life in ways similar to mine. Apart from having negative labels applied to me in my earliest years, I came to realize in the end that I had actually grown up in a marvelously loving environment. I had an intact family with parents who loved each other and who loved their children. My parents didn't smoke or drink. They never swore or told off-color stories or jokes. We all sat down at the table and ate meals together. We prayed together. We learned good manners, true principles, and strict morals. Surely, I thought, every child was raised that way.

I knew of special cases, of course, which must be rare, in which children were abused or molested by family members or by strangers. But I believed that on the whole children came from homes just like mine. Little did I understand the world in which youth grow up today. Either I was completely wrong or those who took my course represented but a small and unfortunate segment of the population.

Here is a typical story of a student: After I had explained the wholesomeness of the intact family and its impact on health and well-being, one girl asked if she could see me in my office after class. She sat down and said, "Dr.

Ainsworth, I'm trying hard to appreciate what you're saying, but this is my problem. When I was a young girl, my father sexually molested me. When I was fourteen years old, my first boyfriend date-raped me. My second boy-friend got me pregnant and skipped town, so I ended up having an abortion. Then, during my first course at SCSU, my professor told me that if I didn't have sex with him I would flunk the class. How can you expect me to love men?"

After that conversation, instead of telling students what I thought their lives should be, I began a crash course on learning about their lives. I allowed them to teach *me* about love and health, which they did admirably well.

They proved to be good teachers indeed, and eventually the course gravitated to what Leo Buscaglia had suggested at the outset: "Sit in a circle and talk a lot." As the years progressed, I realized I was listening more and talking less.

But even when you become good at listening, when you think you've heard

> **LOVE AND COUNTERFEITS**
>
> I want to love you without clutching,
> appreciate you without judging.
> Join you without invading,
> invite you without demanding.
> Leave you without guilt,
> criticize you without blaming.
> If I can have the same from you,
> then we can truly meet and enrich each other.

it all, someone surprises you. One student told the class how she wanted to get back at her boyfriend for having sex with more girls than she had had with guys at a sexual orgy the previous weekend. She asked, "How do I get even with my boyfriend?" After relating this incident and asking the class for advice, twenty-four sets of eyes shifted from her to me. Nothing had prepared me for that moment.

In our course evaluations of Love and Health, students often wrote, "This class should be required for every incoming freshman." Of course, nothing could have been further from the truth. *Requiring* people to learn about love doesn't work. As the whole idea of love is based on free choice, *making* students learn about love is self-contradictory.

Another reason for not making Love and Health a requirement was that, as a rule, freshmen are not ready to learn about love, at least not about romantic love. That was why seniors received priority in their course selections. In fact, whereas the curriculum committee said the course would die from lack of interest, Love and Health was one of the fastest to fill up during class registration.

To properly teach love's relationship to health, one had to involve the whole person in a process of personal development that included mind, body, and spirit. Ours wasn't simply a course on romance. Though we covered that important aspect of love, our goal was to comprehend the totality of love, to determine how it related to our own well-being and to everyone else's around us whom we might influence or affect.

Rollo May, in his book, *Love and Will*, said, "We have reduced love to its lowest level, sex. We have removed the fig leaf from the genitals and placed it over the face." Eric Fromm, in his book, *The Art of Loving*, says we mistake love for sex appeal. As a part of our course, we assessed these statements to determine if they were true. We also delved into the manifold other forms of love.

For years, I found it a challenge to explain the involvement of the mind and the spirit as well as the body in discussing love's relationship to health. But after much struggling I was able to develop a model of total health that appeared to work well.

HEART AND MIND

If the world kept a journal, many of the entries would be conversations concerning the advancement of scientific knowledge and its importance to humanity.

I offer the following conversations as an added entry...

"And what is as important as knowledge?" asked the mind.

"Caring," answered the heart.

Flavia

3

There are no crown-bearers in heaven who
were not cross-bearers here below
—Spurgeon

Twelve Primary Ingredients of Health

As an essential part of the coursework we covered in class, I formulated the idea of twelve primary ingredients of health. These twelve regenerative constituents are so fundamental that you may think them commonplace, but they become increasingly meaningful as we move from the purely physical aspects of health into the entire spectrum of what constitutes well-being in the whole person. In other words, we start with things we're familiar with and go on to learn aspects of health about which, at present, we may not have much idea though they greatly impact our total health.

In that sense, it's fair to say that in actuality there are just *four* primary ingredients of health. We simply replicate them in three different modes of the human experience, namely, as they relate to 1. physical health; 2. mental health; and 3. spiritual health.

Under **Physical Health** we cover food and water, rest, exercise, and elimination. I will treat these four categories individually and point out their essential features. Once again, this initial discussion may seem rudimentary, but you will find it helpful to review these fundamental points before progressing to the perhaps more consequential categories that follow.

Food and Water

   a.   There are four basic food groups: 1. fruits and vegetables; 2. meats; 3. grains; and 4. dairy products. It's essential that you eat from all four. The more your diet relies on just one food group, the more you place your health at risk.

FOOD

b. You can eat too much or too little. Ideally, you should eat only what your body requires, not an excessive amount. Everybody's needs are different but this principle holds true for all.

c. There *is* such a thing as "junk food," and though it may keep you alive, in the long run it won't serve you well. The degree to which a person may eat junk food without undue harm is directly proportional to the amount of healthy foods he or she consumes. So if you eat a healthy diet, say, ninety-five percent of the time, then perhaps you can afford a little junk food five percent of the time.

d. You should eat to live, not live to eat. Foods should never become an addiction, which is a sure sign of an unbalanced diet.

e. The main component of food, and of the human body, is water. We can't say enough about the quality and quantity of water we should drink. Research shows that pure water behaves quite differently than contaminated water, whether the contamination is caused by man, as in chlorine, fluoride, factory chemicals, or other pollutants, or by nature, as in highly mineralized water.

f. The purer the water you consume, the better it facilitates the exchange between nutrients and the various tissues of the body. Drinking lots of pure water results in healthier physical functions.

Rest

a. You need adequate rest so that your body can recuperate from its daily activities.

b. Though there are different ways of getting rest, sleep is the most effective and is essential for good health.

c. If you're unable to sleep, you're probably not incorporating sufficiently one or more of the twelve primary ingredients.

REST

d. You should rest in a clean and healthy environment.

Exercise

a. For exercise to be effective, it's essential you work out frequently; I mean at least two or three times per week. Less than that is inadequate.

EXERCISE

b. Though it would be nice, it's not essential that you *like* the exercise. It will benefit you and improve your health whether you exercise willingly or reluctantly.

c. One of the best kinds of exercise involves the heart, consisting of sustained cardiovascular activity, such as a brisk hour's walk or a half-hour jog.

d. Exercise should be regular and form an established part of your daily routine. It should not be capricious or sporadic.

Elimination

ELIMINATION

a. Waste products result from the previously mentioned physical activities. When we eat, sleep, and exercise, food is converted into energy. As in a combustion engine, there are waste products that need to be eliminated.

b. During any given hour, we rid our bodies of numerous toxins and waste products. These are eliminated in the form of carbon dioxide, perspiration, urine, bowel movements, flaking of the skin, etc.

c. If we were to stop eliminating waste products, we would die. When we don't eliminate them properly, we suffer their ill effects. It doesn't matter how noble our intentions or how busy we are, if we don't remove these toxins they'll begin to poison us, a condition called auto-intoxication. In short, when we ignore the need to eliminate toxins, they will get our attention by causing discomfort, pain, and illness.

d. One area we should always investigate when we're ill is whether waste products are being adequately removed.

I will now discuss these same four primary ingredients as they relate to **Mental Health**. Food for the mind consists of knowledge and information and is as essential to mental health as physical food is to physical health.

Child expert Barry Brazelton says that feeding a child's mind, as in mental stimulation, is as important as feeding his body. When children aren't fed intellectually, they atrophy and develop more slowly. In extreme cases, they die. They may receive all essential vitamins and minerals, etc., but mental stimulation remains just as essential to their well-being. Children to whom parents read books, for example, get fewer illnesses, obtain better grades, and are less likely to take drugs or commit suicide than those to whom parents don't read.

Mental Food

MENTAL FOOD

a. Mental food also consists of four basic "food groups." You should feed the mind knowledge and information about your physical world, your mental and emotional world, your social world, and your spiritual world. As with physical health, one should have a "balanced diet" from these four intellectual food groups. Feeding the mind from just one doesn't serve your mental health well.

b. It is possible to consume too much or too little when feeding the mind, especially when maintaining a balance with your physical and spiritual needs.

c. There *is* such a thing as mental "junk food." When I asked students for an example, they almost unanimously named afternoon TV. I never indicated whether I agreed or not, only that there was such a thing. Everyone should identify his or her own mental junk food and apply the same principle as one would with physical junk food. In other words, one should consume little or none but focus instead on mental food that is nourishing.

d. Mental health, like physical health, is more than the mere absence of disease. It involves a positive effort to raise your level of well-being far beyond not getting ill.

e. Mental "water" facilitates the exchange between you and your physical, intellectual, social, and spiritual worlds. The purer that process is, the healthier your mental faculties will be. By pure, I mean devoid of distortions, falsehoods, prejudice, manipulation, machinations, coercion, and so forth. A mental process unpolluted by the widespread contaminants of this world can be a rare thing nowadays, just like pure water!

f. You achieve fluid purity by maintaining an exchange that is truthful, honest, caring, and direct between all your mental and emotional faculties.

Before listing the different aspects of mental rest, I will make brief digression. In class, I generally began this part of the course by asking, "Take your finger and point to your mind." As a rule, students pointed to their heads, to which I responded, "No, that is your brain. Point to your mind." They then seemed mystified.

There is a body of knowledge emerging that appears to support the idea that the mind encompasses much more than the brain, possibly the whole body. The brain rests while you sleep. The mind does not. Indeed one of the most active periods of the mind occurs during sleep. In his book, *The Heart's Code*, Paul Pearsall documents numerous cases in which recipients of donor organs frequently expressed the feelings and recollections of the person from whom the organ came, especially in the case of a donor heart.

A couple of cases will demonstrate this point. A man receives a heart transplant and, unbeknownst to him, the heart donor had an addiction to Carvel Ice Cream. After the recipient recuperates from the operation, he drives around town and finds himself unable to pass a Carvel Ice Cream shop without stopping for ice cream.

Upon recovery from a heart transplant, a recipient makes love to his wife. At a most delicate moment, he refers to his wife by another name. Some checking reveals that the name he mistakenly called his wife was a term of endearment the donor of the heart had for his wife when they made love.

In short, the mind is different than the brain. Like the body, it needs rest. Some researchers, including myself, believe the mind encompasses the entire body. Because the mind doesn't rest during sleep, when does it rest? Here are some basic rules.

Mental Rest

MENTAL REST

a. Your mind needs adequate rest to recuperate from its daily activities, just as your body does.

b. Though there are various ways to rest your mind, meditation appears the most effective. Walks on the beach or in the woods, or just sitting on the front porch, do much to facilitate meditation.

c. People who meditate twenty minutes per day have substantially fewer instances of illness than those who don't meditate at all.

d. One needs to meditate on a regular basis, ideally in a pure and uncluttered environment for twenty minutes per day.

Mental Exercise

a. We exercise the mind when we put it to work. We call this thinking. Thinking should not be confused with memorizing, which is primarily a function of the brain. I told my class that while universities are supposed to make you think and use your mind, as a rule they require you merely to memorize. Thinking is essential for good mental health and development.

MENTAL EXERCISE

b. Though desirable, it isn't necessary that you *like* mental exercise in order to benefit from it. Thinking, or exercising the mind, helps whether you like it or not.

c. The best kinds of thinking involve creating or inventing things, problem solving, and investigating and applying new and better ways of performing tasks.

d. Ample time should be spent thinking about things of the heart. *All* exercise, physical, mental, and spiritual, should involve the heart. When exercising the mind, we might recall the warning of William Harvey James: "A great many people believe they are thinking when they are merely rearranging their prejudices."

Mental Elimination

a. As with physical health, the activities of learning and thinking produce "waste material" that needs to be eliminated. I'm speaking of byproducts of mental processes such as anxiety, depression, stress, disappointment, frustration, jealousy, anger, and other negative emotions or negative reactions to emotions.

MENTAL ELIMINATION

b. When we don't eliminate mental waste, it will exact a price from us, whether in our bodies, minds, or spirits. It may be difficult to predict where or how such byproducts will manifest themselves, but be assured that they will.

c. Some mental and emotional waste is easier to eliminate than others. With the anger I had towards my university administration, it wasn't difficult to let go when confronted with the possibility of it killing me. Here's a simple method that demonstrates how easy it is to release a negative emotion: Ask yourself what purpose it serves to hold on to this feeling. If you're honest and allow the truth to rise to the surface, you'll be able to answer this question without much trouble.

In my case, anger served no good purpose. Indeed, as do physical pollutants, it caused auto-intoxication. I therefore chose to simply release the emotion. I realize, however, that some issues are so hurtful that it is next to impossible to perform so brief and simple an exorcism. But eliminating most mental toxins is actually that uncomplicated. *You* must decide whether the reason you hold on to hurtful emotions outweighs your reason for letting them go. In the case of the student who had been abused by her father and by others, therapy was necessary. Still, we can let go most mental and emotional waste quite easily without outside help.

    d.   Toxic side effects are a normal part of mental and emotional processes, just as carbon dioxide, perspiration, urine, etc. are a normal part of physical functions. Of themselves, such wastes aren't harmful, only when we don't eliminate them.

Under **Spiritual Health**, we discover the same four primary ingredients as under physical and mental health. Before discussing these, however, it is important to address the scientific perspective of people's spiritual nature. At a presentation she gave in New Haven, Connecticut, Elizabeth Kübler-Ross stated that she and other researchers concluded that it was a scientific fact that people have a spirit. They came to that finding after years of studying what are called out-of-body experiences. The thousands of people they interviewed, who had spiritual experiences when they were clinically dead, describe essentially the same phenomenon of the continuance of life after death.

Helen Wambach's book, *Life Before Life*, describes this association of the spirit and the body. As a psychologist, she conducted an experiment on numerous people under hypnosis. She took them back to the day they were born and had them recall what happened. It surprised many to discover that the events surrounding their birth were well etched in their minds and could be recalled in vivid detail.

Following that experiment, Ms. Wambach conducted another. Under hypnosis, she took more than 700 people back to the time *before* they were born to see what they could recall. Once again, with rare exceptions, her patients were surprised to discover they had distinct recollections and feelings about events that occurred before birth.

The hundreds of subjects of this experiment were adamant that the part of them that remembered these things was their spirit, not their body. In fact, her patients described how their spirit visited their body, or fetus, before becoming connected to it. Everyone in the experiment was precise and consistent as to when that connection occurred. No one mentioned that their spirit got "inside" their body at the time, only that it became "connected" to it.

Wambach's book provides much insight and specifics into this phenomenon. The subjects of the experiment frequently stated that they now realized they had known members of their family in their pre-birth existence.

From such studies, it appears that our spirits existed long before we were born. It also seems clear that we, as spirit beings, had individual identities, intelligence, and capacities or aptitudes. In the words of Truman Madsen, author of *Eternal Man*, "Nothing is something we have never been and never can be."

I consider one of the best books describing the spiritual dimension of human nature to be Gary Zukav's *The Seat of the Soul*. The researchers mentioned above offer experiments, studies, and data. Zukav offers explanations, some with profound and eternal implications.

To continue our analogy with physical and mental food, we discover that "spiritual food" is love. Love is necessary for our very survival as well as essential for our well-being. Like food and water, love isn't a luxury, something we can get along without. We cannot.

> ZUKAV
>
> When I would call Gary Zukav and he was not at home, I would get this message on his answering machine:
>
> "Hello, this is Gary and I'm not in right now, so please leave your name and a phone number so I can return your call. Be sure to tell me who you are, and what you want."
>
> "And unless you think that is easy, most people live their whole lives unable to answer those two questions."

René Spitz, who studied orphanages in New York City in the early 1900s, found that though children received all the physical food they needed and were adequately housed and clothed, more than half died before the age of two. They simply died from a lack of love. No one held them, sang to them, or cuddled them. Those who survived were more apt to present long-term problems than others. Mary Fullmer expresses this well when she says, "An unloved child will do more harm to society than untreated sewage."

Experiments conducted on animals, such as cats, dogs, and sheep that were denied the touch of their mothers, or that were not licked or allowed to be close to them, revealed that these animals died easily or became sickly. If they did survive, they were unable to reproduce or interact well with others of their kind.

I had always thought that the animals' licking process was for cleaning the young. Though that may be a part of it, I now know that it is primarily for *touch*. Infant mammals not touched by other mammals don't do well and frequently die, humans included.

Premature babies put in incubators are an example. Those who have someone reach into the incubator and touch them on a regular basis get sick less often, gain weight faster, and are more likely to survive than those not touched. Ashley Montagu's insightful book, *Touching*, documents the influence of touching in our lives.

> Excerpts from
> TOUCHING
>
> Although we know there are enzymes in mother's milk that strengthen the offspring's immune system, there is some evidence that it may be the touch of breast feeding, or at least partially the touch that increases the off-spring's immunity.
>
> The majority of newborn lambs that are denied licking by their mothers, fail to stand and subsequently die within weeks.
>
> Hand milked cows give more and richer terminal milk, than machine-milked cows.
>
> Given the choice between a mother's touch and food, baby monkeys will invariably choose the touch over food.
>
> When a baby is born, a mother is born. There is considerable evidence that at this time, and for months thereafter, her needs for contact exceed those of the infant.
>
> During the nineteenth century more than half the orphaned infants in their first year died from a disease called marasmus (wasting away). In some orphanages the death rate was 100% during the first two years of life.
>
> In a very old morbid experiment Frederick II wanted to know what language children would be inclined to speak if they never heard a specific language during their infant years. He therefore had dozens of children raised under these conditions (never being spoken to). He never did find out which language they would prefer as all the children died before the age of four.
>
> When newborn babies are exposed to the recorded sounds of a heartbeat they gain weight much faster and have fewer respiratory problems than newborns who are not so exposed.
>
> Ashley Montagu

As reported in James Lynch's book, *Medical Consequences of a Broken Heart*, divorced people who don't smoke cigarettes run the same risk of lung cancer as married people who smoke. Documentation from this and similar studies abounds, including the research Steve Sinatra presents in his book, *Heart Break and Heart Disease*.

Early epidemiological studies showed that women live significantly longer than men. From that data researchers concluded that estrogen prolongs life. But when they further discovered that married men live longer than single men, researchers, using their "scientific" logic, concluded that sleeping with estrogen, too, prolonged life! In reality, it has been an uphill struggle to convince the scientific community that being married is actually healthier than being single.

The fact remains that there is a direct link between love, or the lack of it, and our well-being. Moreover, the primary ingredients of spiritual health parallel those of physical and mental health.

Spiritual Food

a. There are four basic "food groups" from which the spirit receives nourishment. In other words, there are four kinds of love. The Greeks called these 1. familial or family love; 2. filial or brotherly love; 3. erotic or romantic love; and 4. agape, the love of God. As with physical and mental food, it is essential that you have a balanced diet of all four. Leaning towards one "spiritual food group" more than the others will put your health at risk.

SPIRITUAL FOOD

Paradoxically, the basis for these four kinds of love is self-love. I don't mean narcissism, which is a kind of self-infatuation. I mean the wholesome acceptance of, and a deep affection for, yourself. Because your ability to love others functions in direct proportion to your ability to love yourself, ending up in a loving relationship isn't so much a process of *finding* the right person as *being* the right person. When you have a sincere love of yourself, you increase the possibility that love will find you. Additionally, you largely reduce the risk of incurring ill health. As Bernie Siegel affirms, "Happy people seldom get sick."

b. I'm not sure if one can receive or give too much love, though I doubt it. Loving too little, however, is definitely possible. Indeed, I suspect that most problems in the world are the result of a lack of love. An old axiom Bernie Siegel taught me was, "Love is the answer. What is the question?" In other words, whatever the problem is, it can be solved with love. Remember, we're talking about actual love, not one of its counterfeits. It is certainly possible to get too much of a love substitute.

Two thousand years ago, a lawyer posed this question to the Teacher from Galilee, "Master, what is the greatest commandment in the Law?" His answer, "You shall love the Lord your God with all your heart, and with all your soul, and with all your mind. This is the first and great commandment. And the second is like it: You shall love your neighbor as yourself." Jesus thus taught that true love involves the body, mind, and spirit.

While many people are aware of that quotation from Matthew 22:38, few are familiar with the next verse, which says, "On these two commandments hang all the Law and the Prophets." In other words, all the teachings of the Old and New Testament are subsidiaries of these two basic principles of love. Most other commandments would probably not be needed if these two were fully understood and lived.

c. Just as there is physical and mental junk food, so there is spiritual junk food, or "junk love." Common forms are infatuation, lust, and the desire to control and manipulate others. Such substitutes of love can keep you alive but don't serve you well.

The most common form of junk love, especially among the young, is infatuation. This love is based on fantasy, not reality. My students kept asking, "How do you know if it's love or something else?" The simple answer I gave is that time will tell. As a rule, infatuation fades and doesn't last very long. One exception is when infatuated people engage in premarital sex, which tends to mask and prolong this love substitute. A simple way to tell if what you're experiencing is infatuation or love is to keep up a relationship but abstain from sex, then wait and see. Time will reveal the truth about whether or not your relationship is based on love.

On one occasion, when I asked students to share a loving experience, a young man stood up in front of the class and opened a Playboy magazine to the centerfold. Displaying an erotic picture, he said, "This is what love is to me." The scary part was that it was true; that was all love meant to him.

It is not necessarily a religious or puritanical statement to say that postponing sex until marriage is by far the healthiest choice; it is a fact based on years of research of thousands of documented cases. The data show, for example, that the more sexual partners a person has prior to marriage, the greater the risks for any number of unhealthy conditions, physical, mental, and spiritual. Research also shows, however, that sex in an exclusive legal relationship is healthy. Moreover, exclusive relationships have been demonstrated to result in far fewer divorces and their unhappy consequences, especially their life-long detrimental effects on children. To sum up the research in this area, the recommendations are not to have sex until you're married, to restrict your sexual activity to your marriage partner, and then to have plenty of it.

Eric Fromm, in his book, *The Art of Loving*, makes a distinction between love and the *feeling* of love. He uses the example of a father of four who receives his weekly paycheck on Friday afternoons. On his way home from work, he stops at the pub and buys drinks for everyone, which, of course makes him popular with the crowd. He continues this into the night until his paycheck is gone. All this time, he shows the bartender and his friends photos of his family. He explains with tears in his eyes how much he loves them.

Fromm asks, "Does he really love his family?" Certainly not! If he did, he would take his paycheck home, buy them groceries, and pay the house bills. What he has for his family is the *feeling* of love. Even after teaching this in class, and after many days of prolonged discussions, most undergraduates couldn't understand the difference between love and the *feeling* of love. Hollywood had duped them.

Swedenborg wrote, "To will but not to do when the opportunity is there is in reality *not* to will. To love what is good, but not to do so when the possibility is there, is in reality *not* to love."

Love and the feeling of love involve much more than romantic love. Jesus said, "Whoever has my commandments and keeps them, he it is who loves me." Just as the man at the pub declared his love to all who would listen, even to tears, so I have seen churchgoers do the same. They proclaim their love of God and of those around them even to tears, yet when it comes time to "bring home the bacon," they are instead drinking at the pub, so to speak. I don't mean that you have to live a perfect life to prove you have love. Rather, that true love—of yourself and of others—consists of rearranging your priorities so as to enable you to honor and serve those you love. Therein lies happiness and the greatest good anyone can achieve.

We often hear someone say, "I love oranges," or "I love chocolate." But if the orange or chocolate could answer back, it might say, "Sure! You're going to rip off my covering, consume me, then pass most of me out of your body in a few of hours." The person doesn't really *love* these items. He loves how they make him feel. He is really saying, "I love you because I *need* you, in contrast to, "I need you because I *love* you." A wise man once put it this way, "The best relationship is one in which your love for each other exceeds your need for each other."

Stephen Covey, in his book, *Spiritual Roots of Human Relations*, gives sound advice about distinguishing love from infatuation or the *feeling* of love. He says that the heart can make good decisions and give sound advice as well as the brain. The question is, When can the heart, or your emotions, be trusted? Can a young person in love trust what he or she is feeling? Can an older person for that matter?

Covey gives this advice: To the degree that you're in charge of your appetites, you can trust your emotions. To the degree you can't control your appetites, you cannot trust your emotions. The man who drank away his paycheck clearly wasn't the master of his appetites but instead mistook a love substitute for love.

Another aberrant form of love, especially for adults, is the desire to control and manipulate others. Many unhealthy relationships fall under this heading of junk love. Not only does trying to control another person stifle true love, but the purpose of the coercion is seldom realized. If it is, it is usually just a short-lived masquerade. When the mask comes off, the despotism and intimidation that characterize attempts at coercion take over. As Gerald Jampolsky says, "Peace of mind comes from *not* wanting to change others."

Without doubt, the healthiest kind of love is *unconditional* love. While for most of us that kind of love doesn't happen at least until our first child is born, it can nevertheless occur at any time. The freshmen and sophomores in my class all swore they had unconditional love. Thirty-year-old graduate students, on the other hand, who were usually married and had children, were not so sure. Forty-year-olds, also mostly married, *knew* their spousal love wasn't unconditional. The rare sixty-year-old student said, "I'm finally getting to the point where I love my spouse unconditionally."

Learning to love, like any other skill, takes time and practice. Mastering the "skill" of loving involves listening to your heart, which can take life-long practice. As Ashley Montagu notes, "There is a genius of the heart which is vastly more valuable than the accomplishment of any other form of genius." Love is, after all, a heart thing.

d. To properly feed your spirit, you must have a loving relationship within all four spiritual "food groups," namely familial, filial, romantic, and agape. As indicated, you must also distinguish love from its counterfeits, which abound in all four categories.

e. The "water" that flows from your spiritual functions is similar to physical and mental water. It is the fluidity with which your four "food groups" of love interface or maintain balance with one another. It constitutes the life force most cultures believe in, which is variously called Chi by the Chinese, Prana by Indians, Ix by the Maya, and the "breath of life" in the Book of Genesis.

   f.   The purer you are—physically, mentally, and spiritually—the better all four kinds of love can function. That purity, or sanctity, is attained by inviting and allowing the life force of the universe to flow through you, purifying your thoughts, words, and actions. If you're not able to access that power, then you can start with giving reverence to its byproducts, such as flowers, beauty, art, music, and so forth. Native Americans learned long ago that being in tune with the four elements of earth, air, water, and fire was a way of gaining access to the Great Spirit or one's benevolent higher power.

The Teacher from Galilee said, "Consider the lilies, how they grow. They don't toil nor spin. And yet, I say to you that Solomon in all his glory was not arrayed like one of these." Putting this statement in context, if the temple of Solomon were built today it would cost more than ten billion dollars. But the Jewish Master understood that wild lilies possess more beauty, purity, and life than did that magnificent ancient edifice. When we can appreciate this principle and apply it in our lives, then will pure spiritual water flow through us of its own accord without our having to "make it happen." The pure exchange of love will become second nature and we will experience an abiding peace.

Spiritual Rest

SPIRITUAL REST

   a.   We rest spiritually when we commune with a higher power. For most of us, that means communicating with God, as in worship services and public and private prayer. For others, it may involve staying in touch with nature or some other higher power.

The spirit, like the mind and body, needs rest. In our Judeo-Christian society, the commonly prescribed way to rest spiritually is to reserve one day of the week to commune with God. In fact, Judaism teaches that if you rest completely one day in seven, uncluttered by everyday pursuits, you never need a vacation. The word Sabbath itself comes from the verb "to cease," that is, to cease from mundane activities.

Contrary to popular belief, there is ample evidence to show the positive effect of a Sabbath day of rest. A study published by Yale University in the 1990s reports how researchers followed some 2800 women for twenty-eight years, measuring all indices they thought might provide insight into their health and well-being. They discovered that those who regularly attended religious services tended to be much healthier than those who didn't. After factoring out everything that could have contributed to this difference, such as churchgoers eating better, exercising more, and so forth, the group that attended religious services stood out from the rest.

The researchers who conducted this study, who were not necessarily religious themselves, and who certainly were not looking for that kind of result, were astonished. They had no explanation other than that attending religious services was a healthy thing to do. How healthy was it? They said that *not* attending regular religious services had a negative effect on health equivalent to smoking a pack of cigarettes daily. Need we say more? Resting the spirit is as important as resting the mind and body.

 b. The most common way of communing with God is through prayer, as in offering prayers of thanksgiving or petition. Dr. Larry Dossey has published over a dozen books showing the measurable health effects of prayer. He reports that in study after study, hospital patients were divided into two groups. One group was then prayed for but not the other. Of course, neither group knew who was being prayed for; nor did physicians and nurses. With rare exception, the group prayed for recovered from their illnesses quicker than those not prayed for.

After numerous such studies, Dr. Dossey concluded that it is irrelevant how near or how far away the group is that is prayed for. Nor does the religious affiliation matter of those who pray or of those who are prayed for; the process appears to work equally well for all. Research shows that our prayers have the same positive effect regardless of what religion we belong to or even whether we belong to one at all.

As odd as it may sound, this same result is true for *all* living organisms, human or non-human. Plants that are prayed for grow faster and are healthier than those not prayed for. Even single-cell organisms, microbes, bacteria, and so forth, have been shown to be influenced by prayer. The scientific evidence is overwhelming—prayer works.

With each passing year, more and more medical schools are incorporating these non-traditional kinds of data into their medical curricula. I don't recall where I heard the following statement but it sounds apropos: "Prayer is the most unused skill in the world and faith the most untapped power."

c. There are a variety of ways we can commune with God or with a higher power. Ideally, these should complement one another. Religious activities should feed the spirit in a safe and wholesome environment and not open one up to lower influences that are prone to take advantage of a situation. Uplifting literature, art, and music aid one's spiritual renewal. Regular social activities in the company of spiritually minded folk regenerate the spirit. But spiritual counterfeits abound also, so beware.

d. When communing with your higher power, don't forget to listen. The responses you get may surprise and delight you—they're intended to do just that. The impulses you feel when praying may guide you towards a more fulfilling life to the point that you are in constant touch with a higher power that loves, directs, and protects you. You may then attain the immense satisfaction of understanding the purpose of your life.

Spiritual Exercise

a. The way we exercise the spirit is to serve and assist others. The rules for this are about the same as for exercising the mind and body. For the exercise to be meaningful, it should be regular, not sporadic or capricious. Though random acts of kindness are desirable and healthy, I'm speaking of something more measurable and significant.

SPIRITUAL EXERCISE

For example, I adopted a personal policy of tithing my time. In addition to putting in a forty-hour workweek, I mentored students who needed counseling free of charge for four hours per week. Currently, after retiring from my teaching profession, I spend even more time in voluntary social service.

b. As with physical exercise, it isn't necessary that you enjoy the service you render in order to gain the benefit of it. Years ago, when I took a class with Stephen Covey, he taught three rules: 1. know the right thing to do; 2. do the right thing; and 3. do the right thing for the right reason. Years later, when listening to Covey make a presentation, he said he had modified his rules as follows: 1. know the right thing to do; 2. do the right thing; and 3. do the right thing for the best reason you can come up with. Similarly, service doesn't need to be done for the right reasons to have a positive health benefit. I'm convinced, however, that if you do the right thing long enough it will lead you to the point where eventually you will be doing it for the right reason. The important thing is to do it.

In some experiments, when students were shown photographs of Mother Teresa working in Calcutta, their immune systems immediately improved. They produced more killer T cells, more white blood cells, and so forth. In her lifetime of serving the under-privileged, she became an illustrious example what her Galilean Teacher taught: "He who would be the greatest among you will be your servant." Exercising the spirit by serving others is as essential to a person's health as exercising the mind and body.

c. The best kind of exercise always involves the heart. I'm not talking about cardiovascular conditioning in this case but of learning to love others deeply for themselves, for who they are. The service you render them will itself generate your love for them. Parents grow to love their children when they serve them to the best of their ability. It is in giving that we receive and in loving that we are loved. If you want to learn to love someone, then serve that person. Love *will* follow.

d. As a rule, what you do at work doesn't count as service. When I gave a presentation of the twelve primary ingredients of health to a group of nurses at a hospital a few years ago and mentioned the idea of serving others, some assumed they had that covered because of the nature of their work. But service on a job for which you get paid isn't the same thing as giving of your personal time, energy, and resources. Paid service doesn't count for the same reason physical exercise at work doesn't count. Though people may walk up and down stairs in the work place, and though that helps keep them active to some degree, they must still do their quota of walking, jogging, or whatever they do for aerobic exercise before or after work. For service to be real, beneficial, and healing to the soul, it must be voluntary.

e. Those who don't serve others in this manner can't reap its health benefits. Refusing to serve others, for example, is called selfishness. Neal Maxwell puts this in perspective when he says, "Selfishness is really self-destruction in slow motion." It portrays an unhealthy mindset and lifestyle and constitutes another way of dying.

Spiritual Elimination

SPIRITUAL ELIMINATION

a. As you apply the principles I have mentioned, it is inevitable that lapses will occur, whether from others offending us or from us offending others. The effects of these lapses are normal byproducts of life, toxins that inevitably arise from living with other people. These waste products, however, must be eliminated or they will cause the same kinds of harm as physical and mental toxins.

b. We eliminate spiritual wastes by forgiving others and ourselves. Of the two, the second seems the most difficult as people often beat up on themselves. Either that or they have no regrets whatever for what they do wrong. I believe it was Benjamin Franklin who said, "It doesn't surprise me to see men sin, but it surprises me to see them have no remorse for it."

c. A person has two choices with regard to forgiveness. He can either resolve an issue that warrants forgiveness or leave it unresolved and pay dearly for it later. It is infinitely easier and a much healthier choice, however, to resolve and release it.

d. Forgiveness may require that you go to someone whom you have wronged, or who has wronged you, and settle the matter. That doesn't mean you have to agree with the person, only that you freely forgive him or her as well as yourself and let go of the issue. For some of us, that may require seeking help from our minister, priest, or rabbi.

An incident I experienced will demonstrate what I'm saying. I lived in a condominium complex. And as anyone who has lived in one knows, one of the greatest "sins" is to park in someone else's parking space. In our area, this is such a sensitive issue that if someone parks in your space a phone call to a member of the board results in the car being promptly towed away at the owner's expense.

One day, when I came home from work, a car was parked in my space. As I didn't recognize the car, I assumed it was someone visiting a neighbor who didn't know where visitors' parking spots were. Either that or they were having a party. In any event, I parked in a visitor's spot that day, assuming the car would be gone the next morning. It wasn't.

I thought, "This must be some party." I was sure the car would be gone when I returned home from work that evening. It wasn't. The strange car was still parked in my space. I knocked on doors to see if anyone knew who owned the car. Sometimes stolen cars are abandoned this way. No one seemed to know. So I called a member of the board and had it towed, of course at the owner's expense, which meant a $35 fee.

The day after I had the car towed, my next-door neighbor knocked on my door and told me I owed him $35 for having his brother's car towed. His brother had stayed at his place while he and his wife were on vacation. His brother didn't know the correct parking space and therefore could not be held responsible for following the rules. I don't need to rehearse the complete conversation to describe where it led. It ended by my neighbor saying we could no longer be friends until I reimbursed him the $35.

For the next few weeks, my neighbor would pass me and not speak. Of course, I would chuckle inside, like I really cared! Then, strange things began happening to my car. I had a cherry-condition 1964 Mustang convertible. First, the hubcaps would fall off when I left for work in the morning. Then I would discover that my lug nuts were loose. All this time my neighbor would remind me that I owed him $35.

Finally, one morning I was about to get in my car when I noticed someone had run a knife blade down the side of my car and made a deep gash in the original paint work. I assumed all these pranks were my neighbor's doing but I had no proof. I spent $1,200 having the car repainted only to have the same thing happen on its other side a week later. Once again I paid $1,200.

At this point in the story, I usually asked my class, "Given these circumstances, what would you do?" Remember, I only suspected this was being done by my neighbor; I had no proof he was the culprit. You can imagine the students' responses, especially from the males.

I then told them how I resolved this. I applied the principle of Stephen Covey's book, *Seven Habits of Highly Successful People.* I went to John and asked him to explain why he thought I owed him $35. He was from the old country and had different ideas about these things. After listening to him for an hour, I finally understood why he felt the way he did. I didn't agree with him but I understood him. At that point, I reached into my pocket, pulled out $35, and gave it to him. I then said, "Now please leave my car alone." He just smiled. Nothing untoward happened to my car after that.

When I shared this story with my students, most disagreed with what I did. They said, "It's a matter of principle." I said, "You're right. But which principle?" I could easily have harmed his car as badly as mine, or worse. Given enough time pursuing what our egos dictated we could have been shooting at each other by now. I then asked how they thought the conflict in the Middle

East, or almost anywhere else in the world, had started.

When I asked my students what my biggest mistake in this incident was they seldom understood. It cost me $2,400 before I figured it out myself. My neighbor truly felt he had been wronged and it took only an hour of listening and $35 to resolve it. But the good part is that my next-door neighbor then became the very person who looked after my place when I traveled, taking in my mail, or painting my screen door when needed. He was right, we could be good neighbors only if I understood his point of view. It was the best $35 I ever spent!

In the words of Leo Aikman, "The golden rule is of no use whatever unless you realize it's your move." Chapin was even more poignant when he wrote, "Never does the human soul appear so strong and noble as when it forgoes revenge and dares to forgive an injury."

This discussion of forgiveness would be incomplete without addressing the forgiveness of our parents. First, we should understand that none of us has perfect parents. With rare exceptions, however, we had parents who loved us. All we could expect of them was to raise us to the best of their ability. Still, being human, their efforts would unavoidably fall short of perfection. At some point, therefore, we must come to terms with that reality.

Years ago, when I studied counseling, Victor Brown taught me that if your parents' or anyone else's behaviors have caused you pain, and you choose not to resolve it with them, then you are a "professional victim." I'm not talking about serious offenses like sexual abuse but of common hurtful foibles.

The professional victim is one who hangs on to his or her pain, complaining about it constantly, serving a personal need to do so. When you choose to do that you can no longer lay the blame on the offender, on your parents, or on anyone else. You now personally own the cause of your pain. You own it because you understand the cause, can resolve it through forgiveness, but choose not to do so. Such people actually prefer pain to enjoying wholeness or well-being. In other words, some individuals aren't happy unless they're miserable! Dr. Laura stated it this way, "First you're a victim, but after that you're a volunteer."

Forgiving and resolving issues is one of the healthiest things we can do, whether for ourselves or for the community we live in. How many conflicts exist in the world and how many people have been killed because two people failed to sit down and resolve their differences, differences that initially were probably no more complex than the one I just shared with you.

And while on the subject of forgiveness, do you remember the vice-president of the university who fired me as director of my division? Two years later, he was fired as vice-president! And I think he was just as hurt and angry as I was. Like me, he was put back as a regular faculty member into the academic department from which he came. The office they assigned him happened to be in the same building into

---

LET GO

To "Let Go" does not mean to stop caring; it means I can't do it for someone else.

To "Let Go" is not to cut myself off; it's the realization that I can't control another.

To "Let Go" is not to enable, but to allow learning from natural consequences.

To "Let Go" is to admit powerlessness, which means the outcome is not in my hands.

To "Let Go" is not to try to change or blame another; it's to make the most of myself.

To "Let Go" is not to care for, but to be supportive.

To "Let Go" is not to judge, but to allow another to be a human being.

To "Let Go" is not to be in the middle arranging all the outcomes, but to allow others to affect their own destinies.

To "Let Go" is not to be protective; it's to permit another to face reality.

To "Let Go" is not to deny, but to accept.

To "Let Go" is not to nag, scold or argue, but instead to search out my own shortcomings and correct them.

To "Let Go" is not to adjust everything to my desires, but to take each day as it comes, and to cherish myself in it.

To "Let Go" is not to criticize and regulate anybody but to become what I dream I can be.

To "Let Go" is not to regret the past, but to grow and live for the future.

To "Let Go" is to fear less, and love more.

which I was trying to move my new faculty. By that time, I was again serving as a program coordinator. But I couldn't get permission to occupy the offices because the administration was afraid to put Bob and me in the same building.

So I went to Bob, shook his hand, and asked him to forgive me for the hurts I had caused him. I assured him I had no more bad feelings towards him. That freed us up to occupy office space in the same building. It also started Bob and me playing golf together. Finally, Bob partly dedicated one of his recent books to me. That is the way these kinds of silly conflicts should end, or rather, begin.

Forgiveness is the saving grace of all the other ingredients of health. When you haven't been living one of them perfectly, forgive yourself and begin again. When someone hurts you, forgive him or her. Release the anger you have and allow the toxins to flow out. Forgiveness is in actuality an act of love. If you love others for any length of time, it will eventually be necessary to forgive them for something. That being the case, you may as well start working at it now so that when you're called upon to forgive something big you'll be ready. Like any other skill, it takes practice.

The truth is that most people don't know how to forgive. They often *think* they've forgiven someone a wrong when in reality they still harbor resentments in their hearts. These resentments or toxins continue festering and cankering the spirit until one becomes spiritually, emotionally, and even physically ill. They're proof that forgiveness still needs to happen.

One of the most effective ways to forgive is to declare it out loud to yourself while being as specific as you can. This simple formula works well: "I (say your name), forgive (say the name of the offender) for (describe the offense)." You can do this while driving your car alone. If you're embarrassed other drivers may see you, pretend you're speaking into your cell phone, or whatever works for you. As you go down the list of people and things for which you want to forgive others, you will feel the spiritual wastes drain away. A clean, pure and wholesome feeling will replace the old anxiety and you will wonder why you hadn't done this a long time ago!

Don't forget to forgive yourself—using the same formula—for the dumb things *you* have done. Many resentments we harbor are caused by our own stupidities and the uncomfortable memory we have of them. Then, should you ever feel them cropping up again, repeat the process until eventually they're gone forever.

I learned a principle of "loving behavior" towards others in Stephen Covey's class many years ago. He explained that we ought always to act in a loving way, whether in our families, workplace, or community. He asked us to practice it for a week and then report back to him. The reports were disastrous. Students rehearsed how, when they attempted loving others, they had been taken advantage of. He asked what kind of loving behavior had caused such awful results. A few of us explained what we had done. Stephen said, "I asked you to behave in a loving, not in a stupid way." Love isn't a process of allowing someone to abuse you or walk over you. It is a process of interacting with others in an honest, empathetic, and caring way. All the while, remembering to extend the same courtesy to yourself.

To sum up what we've discussed thus far, here are the twelve primary ingredients of health in a nutshell:

Physical Health	Mental Health	Spiritual Health
Food & Water	Knowledge/Information	Loving Self and Others
Rest	Meditation	Communing with God
Exercise	Thinking	Serving Others
Elimination	Letting Go	Forgiving Self and Others

By applying these twelve healthful ingredients in our lives we FREE ourselves from physical, mental, and spiritual maladies and allow ourselves to become whole. The regenerative principles they teach can also be used as a tool for making any personal health assessment: How am I doing in this or that area? What should I focus on most right now? Where did this current problem originate? And so forth. You will amaze yourself as you assimilate each of these constituents of wholesome living and reap the benefits that follow.

THE PROPHET
by Kahlil Gibran

Then said Almitra, Speak to us of Love.
   And he raised his head and looked upon the people, and there fell a stillness
upon them. And with a great voice he said:
When love beckons to you, follow him, though his ways are hard and steep.
   And when his wings enfold you, yield to him, though the sword hidden among his pinions may wound you.
And when he speaks to you believe in him, though his voice may shatter your dreams as the north wind lays waste the garden.

For even as love crowns you, so shall he crucify you.
   Even as he is for your growth, so is he for your pruning.
Even as he ascends to your height and caresses your tenderest branches that quiver in the sun,
So shall he descend to your roots and shake them in their clinging to the earth.

Like sheaves of corn, he gathers you unto himself.
   He threshes you to make you naked.
   He sifts you to free you from your husks.
   He grinds you to whiteness.
   He kneads you until you are pliant;
And then he assigns you to his sacred fire, that you may become bread for God's sacred feast.

All these things shall love do unto you that you may know the secrets of your heart, and in that knowledge become a fragment of Life's heart.

4

Adversity is the diamond dust heaven polishes its jewels with
—Leighton

The Relationship Between Body, Mind, and Spirit

Because we are made up of body, mind, and spirit, we can't isolate one part of us from another but must consider all three together. The desires of the body—its appetites, cravings, and lusts—for example, are juxtaposed with the desires of the spirit. The body wants its needs satisfied, whether for food, drink, drugs, sleep, sex or any of its appetites or addictions. The cry of the body is always, "Satisfy me now." Not having our physical needs met can cause anxiety and frustration and put us on edge. It can even ignite anger and aggression where deeper issues have been left unresolved to now

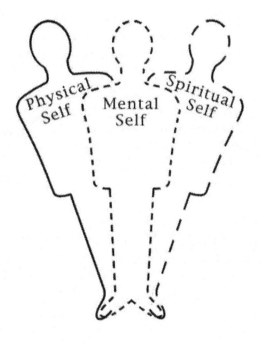

team up with physical discomfort into an emotional outburst or temper tantrum.

The spirit, on the other hand, says, "You don't need that much." Or, "You don't need it right now." Or, "You don't need it at all." This is the perpetual battle that goes on between body and spirit. It isn't that the spirit doesn't want the desires of the body satisfied; it simply wants to maintain a healthy balance.

The spirit wants joy and happiness, which are long-term rewards, whereas the body wants satiation and pleasure or short-term rewards.

The mind is the battleground where this engagement, or even conflict, takes place. The mind is the synapse between body and spirit (see illustration). Unlike the body and spirit, however, the mind doesn't care which side wins. It simply carries out the desires of the winner. As in a political arena, however, if the mind sees the body always winning, it begins to align itself with the physical part of the person. But if the spirit does most of the winning, then the mind aligns itself with the spiritual part. The mind, as a go-between, is thus open to negotiation for which side of the person it gives its allegiance.

Because the origin of the spirit is eternal and divine, its allegiance is to eternal and divine truth and eternal principles. You can therefore always trust the spirit to give you the right answers for direction in your life. The spirit is the part of you most closely aligned with God, nature, or whatever part of the universe you consider supreme. Juvenal expressed this well: "Never does nature say one thing and wisdom another."

The body, on the other hand, says, "I want what I want when I want it." This doesn't mean the body is bad, only that it has different priorities than the spirit. If the body didn't want food, drink, and sleep, we couldn't exist. But a proper *balance* between all the ingredients of health is necessary for our well-being. The spirit knows best how to establish and maintain this balance.

One of the greatest things we can achieve in life is learning to listen to the spirit and disciplining ourselves to follow its counsel. The "voice of the universe" speaks to us through our spirit. That is one reason we often receive inspiration or revelation

---

SIGNS AND SYMPTOMS OF INNER PEACE

- A tendency to think and act spontaneously rather than on fears based on past experiences.

- An unmistakable ability to enjoy each moment.

- A loss of interest in judging other people.

- A loss of interest in conflict.

- A loss of the ability to worry. (This is a very serious symptom)

- Frequent, overwhelming episodes of appreciation.

- Contented feelings of connectedness with others and nature.

- Frequent attacks of smiling.

- An increasing tendency to let things happen rather than make them happen.

- An increased susceptibility to the love extended by others as well as the uncontrollable desire to extend it.

Gerald Jampolsky

when in a sleep, semi-sleep, or meditative state. At that point, the body has relinquished control, allowing the spirit to be in charge. Over time, as our spirit gains the upper hand, we're able to tune in more and more to God, the Great Spirit or higher power we access whenever the need arises. Consequently, we can align ourselves much better with eternal and divine truth than if the physical side of us were in control.

This battle between spirit and body isn't unique to our generation. The Apostle Paul describes it when he counsels Christians in Rome to "walk not after the flesh but after the spirit." The practice of fasting—of denying the body its sustenance for a brief period of time—for example, allows the spirit to be in charge. It teaches the body a lesson that it somehow needs to learn over and over. If that lesson is not learned, imbalance will result.

One author had another way of expressing this struggle: "There are two kinds of matter, that which acts and that which is acted upon." In order to maintain a person's balance and well-being, the ideal relationship between the two is for that which acts—the spirit—to dictate behavior to that which is acted upon, or the body. When that relationship is perfected, then the physical matter that is acted upon becomes more like the spirit and can thus ultimately become the same pure and noble kind of matter that the spirit is.

A worst-case scenario would be to reverse this process, to have the matter that should be acted upon—the body—control the matter that should be in charge, or the spirit. Under this category, for example, comes the immense harm drug addiction does to a human being, whether the drug be legal or illegal. The addict is controlled by the substance his body craves or that he believes he can't do without. Therefore, one shouldn't take into account only the *physical* harm drugs may do, when their *spiritual* harm may be far greater.

The more a person becomes subject to chemicals, from whatever source they derive, the more those substances wrest control from the spirit and surrender it to the body. The results of this can be disastrous. Imbalance, however, can arise just as well from food, lust, or any other physical appetite that dominates a person's life.

If you've played sports, you know that there are fundamental skills you must master that are peculiar to each sport. But once you've mastered them, you can then adapt your style, personality, and predilections to any contest. Each accomplished player, in other words, demonstrates his or her own genius at the game. Each has his or her own unique aptitude for the sport and a unique set of talents that are brought to bear.

Health and well-being work the same way. There are fundamental skills in maintaining physical, mental, and spiritual health that one must master. But once having learned them, we can express our peculiar likes and dislikes to our hearts' content. None of us was intended to be a stereotype. Nor need we become specimens of humanity who are unlikable or unlovable. Our individual personalities are *us*, expressing the unique persons we are and the unique talents we bring to humanity's table. In fact, we can go so far as to say that in our spiritual or higher state the world not only needs us but can't do without us. We each have a noble contribution to make that benefits society as a whole and also us personally. We don't all have to go to Calcutta, like Mother Theresas, as there are ample needs in every community.

The secret is to be in tune with your spiritual inclinations. When that alignment is in effect, you will always be exposed to "coincidences" that invite your love and assistance. Coincidences are God's way of remaining anonymous.

The greatest mastery of life, then, is unquestionably the mastery of self— keeping our desires, appetites, and passions under our spirit's direction and control. That noble part of us knows the truth because it has access to the divine and is able to guide and direct us at all times. It is through subjecting our bodies to our spirits, in fact, that we distinguish ourselves from the animal kingdom.

To help students understand these differences, I drew a distinction between a 1. human doing; 2. human thinking; and 3. human being. When appetites dictate our behavior, we are "*doing* our own thing," so to speak, driven by our physical or animal nature. On the next highest level, principles, concepts, and rational *thinking* motivate and inspire us, separating us from the rest of creation. On the highest level, we move from figuring out and assimilating true principles into following our hearts, our spiritual self. At that point, truth has become an integral part of us—it is written in our hearts and permeates our *being.* It defines who we are, not what we do. On this level, we're motivated by love and are in full possession of ourselves. We *are* or exist because we love, and are in love, with the universe. We are, in full measure of the term, a Human Being. This is the source of lasting happiness.

The story is told of a university that had a Platonic quote inscribed on an arch above the entrance to its campus. It said, "Know thyself." One night, a prankster, who may have been as wise as Plato, painted through the word "Know" and in its place wrote, "Behave." (Behave Thyself) The rascally vandal may have gotten it right.

As we experience this internal tug-of-war, we ideally pass through a process of self-mastery that greatly increases our self-love and thus our ability to love others. Because both loves are essentially a spiritual process, anything that detracts from spiritual growth and sustenance unavoidably inhibits our ability to love and to receive love.

Although love is primarily a spiritual activity, in its full flower it involves the totality of our functions—body, mind, and spirit. Breaking things down to their fundamentals, however, we find that it is the spirit that initiates and sustains love, not the mind; and certainly not the body. Mary Calderon once said, "Boys play with love to get sex, while girls play with sex to get love." Because their goals are centered more around love, females tend to have a great natural affinity for love than males. The males' goal, too often, is self-gratification.

The spiritual or higher part of us hungers and thirsts for truth, for a knowledge of things as they are, as distinct from what we or others may presume they are. Truth is intimately connected with love because it informs us what to love and how to love. The person who loves others best is one who knows them better—who is in tune with them and their needs enough to understand their situation—and who then does what needs doing, or says what needs saying.

Lastly, loving someone is synonymous with being open and truthful with that person. Being untruthful or deceitful is one of the great counterfeits of love. We deceive and manipulate others because we are interested in having our own needs met rather than theirs, which attitude is the opposite of love. Persons who are possessive, or who love material things, moreover, tend to act in that way at the expense of feeding their spirit.

Some people maintain that there is no such thing as truth—that everything in life is relevant. Indeed, there were professors at my university who made that assertion. I preferred not to quarrel with them. My position still is, Tell me things as they were, as they are, and as they will be. Call that what you wish; to me it's truth. Don't make me guess what the facts are when you're speaking with me. The responsibility for that belongs to you, the speaker, not the listener.

Of course, an integral part of our need for truth is to love ourselves enough to be truthful with ourselves. It is difficult to be truthful with others when you're deceiving yourself. By practicing self-deception, we create imbalance between our spirit, mind, and body. Need I say that when we subject ourselves to lies, we become beholden to them? The Teacher from Galilee taught, "The truth shall make you free"—not free to do your own thing, but free from spiritual, mental, and physical bondage—free to exercise pure love. To quote King Arthur's motto of the Roundtable, "God grant us the wisdom to discover the right [the truth], the will to choose it, and the strength to make it endure." That is love.

Because serving others is the ultimate act of love, we can't serve them when we live lives of distortion, manipulation, or control. As these behaviors seek to make others dependent on us, to conform them to *our* way of thinking and acting, they're misleading in their conception and destructive in their implementation. In a word, they rob both us and them of freedom. Santayana uses the perfect metaphor to express the principle on which love operates: "Love is like the sun, it warms and encompasses everything but restricts nothing."

COMES THE DAWN

After a while you learn the subtle difference
between holding a hand and chaining a soul.
And you learn that love doesn't mean security;
and you begin to learn that kisses aren't contracts,
and presents aren't promises.
And you begin to accept your defeats
with your head up and your eyes open,
with the grace of a woman, not the grief of a child.
And you learn to build all your roads on today,
because tomorrow's ground is too uncertain.
And futures have a way of falling down in mid-flight.
After a while you learn that even sunshine burns
if you get too much.
So you plant your own garden and decorate your own
soul,
instead of waiting for someone to bring you flowers.
And you find that you really can endure…
That you really are strong,
And you learn and learn.
With every goodbye you learn.
And then, finally then, love is ready for you.

Author Unknown

5

Gold is tried by fire, people by adversity
—Seneca

Ten Behavioral Principles

Some basic guidelines help us live the twelve ingredients of health and deal with the spiritual–physical conflict discussed above. These behavioral principles identify the human qualities we need to maintain if we want to achieve physical, mental, and spiritual health and achieve lasting happiness. Fuzziness about such matters leads people to take the easy road, which carries its own hazards. As the poet said, "Following the path of least resistance makes both rivers and men crooked."

I once knew a person who was incapable of telling the truth. She had lied or exaggerated so consistently most of her life that it had become more natural for her to distort the truth than to admit it. Even when telling the truth would have served her purpose better, she had become incapable of doing so and would still lie and exaggerate because that was her normal behavior.

We must at some point decide whether truth, honesty, virtue, and so forth are qualities we want to incorporate in our lives. If not, we won't be able to achieve the balance and well-being we are capable of. Once we decide yes, however, then the following principles will be helpful to consider:

1. One cannot store away healthy or wholesome behavior to be drawn upon at some point later in life, as in a bank account. The young lady I mentioned believed in telling the truth, but only in theory, because it was seldom convenient for her to be honest. When questioned about this, she would answer (like Scarlet O'Hara, in *Gone With The Wind*), "I'll start that tomorrow." Truth was a quality she "laid aside" for use later in life, when she assumed it would become more convenient or easier for her to accept. That idea was itself a distortion, but this was not at all obvious to her. She was never able to access the truth on any consistent basis because the truth was not a part of who she was. It could be found nowhere in her persona because the physical and mental parts of her had long overruled the spiritual.

Once, while teaching at a university, a rather risqué play came to campus and several students asked if I planned to attend. When I said no, they wanted to know my reasons. After I explained why I wasn't interested in that sort of entertainment, a student responded, "That is beautiful. I believe that when I'm your age I'll feel like that too." In my case, of course, I had worked many years to cultivate the kind of philosophy that determined my behavior. But the student believed he could somehow "store away" moral and ethical principles and then bring them out of storage later in life and suddenly put them into full-blown action.

Life doesn't operate that way. As with physical fitness and mental skills, one has to work at applying true principles regularly and consistently in order to build up strength and endurance. Only then does it become second nature and a normal part of your behavior. Then, when something spiritual comes along, something virtuous, lovely, or of good report, or praise worthy, you have strength and wisdom to say yes, to accept that quality into your life or association. That is the food from which your spirit is nourished and the practice from which you develop fundamental spiritual skills.

2. In order to develop and maintain good personal qualities, you have to exercise them consistently throughout your life. You must set a standard of behavior based on the truth, and then do all you can to keep it. Just as it is unarguable that we have to eat well and exercise regularly to develop and maintain our physical well-being, so the same holds true for the mental and spiritual parts of us. But because the mind and spirit are less visible or apparent, we tend not to be reminded that the same principles apply. When you don't feed and water a plant, it starts to wilt. But when our minds and spirits aren't watered, the wilting may go unnoticed and quickly degenerate into an unhealthy condition.

Some years ago, while on an archaeological search in Mexico, I fell from a cliff while climbing a mountain and seriously injured my knee. As a result, I was compelled to stop playing racquetball and golf. During the next six years of performing no significant exercise, I gained a pound per month in weight for a total of seventy pounds. Just as this can happen to the body, so it does to the mind and spirit. When we don't exercise them constantly, they become fat and unhealthy—not all at once, of course, but in small increments, like a pound per month.

3. Personal qualities don't mean much until they're tested and challenged by adversity. It's easy to say, "I've never murdered anyone." But this statement has little substance unless you've been confronted with an incident in which someone really harmed you or a person close to you, when the emotions raging inside you called for revenge, but you didn't yield to them. If at such a time you chose not to retaliate, not to kill or harm the offender but rather to forgive him, then your words carry meaning indeed.

As a wise poet once said,

> It's easy enough to be virtuous
>> When nothing tempts you to stray,
> When without or within no voice of sin
>> Is luring your soul away.
> But it is only an averred virtue
>> Until it is tried by fire,
> And the soul that is worth
>> All the treasures of earth
> Is the soul that controls desire.

4. The best time to decide about incorporating good qualities in your life is before the test arrives. We must determine not to participate in harmful and unhealthy behavior before the temptation presents itself. When you postpone making up your mind, circumstances decide for you. Because one mistake tends to rapidly lead to others—like a woven fabric unraveling—seldom will indecision benefit you. In fact, indecision is itself a decision: a negative one.

If you're undecided whether or not you'll catch the 9:00 a.m. train, then by 9:01 a.m. your indecision has become a decision—you won't board the train. If you're undecided whether you're going to be honest, truthful, or moral in each of your behaviors, then very likely you will not be. Peter Drucker stated it this way: "Unless a decision is reduced to action, it is not a decision at all; it is merely an intention."

As discussed above, honesty, truthfulness, and moral virtue are key qualities of love. When I asked students to list ten characteristics of love, these three were the first they mentioned. Translated into practice, this means that to the degree you are honest, truthful, and moral—both with yourself and with others—the more loving a person you are. And the more loving a person you are, the more spiritual you are. And the more spiritual you are, the healthier you are and the happier you will be. In the words of a philosopher, "It is impossible to take the right attitude towards truth and the wrong attitude towards man."

5. When you improve one personal quality, you automatically improve the others. Years ago, I enlisted a friend as an adjunct professor to teach a course on mental health. Tony worked at a mental health clinic and was a dynamic teacher. He was also a clear thinker and someone whom I admired immensely. Early one morning, he called and asked me to arrange the chairs in his classroom in a special way for his class that evening. He was going to demonstrate a Tavistock group process.

Unfortunately, I completely forgot about his request, so later that evening I received a phone call. As soon as I knew it was Tony, I realized I had forgotten to arrange his chairs. As he explained the problem my lapse in memory had caused him, my mind was working overtime to come up with a face-saving explanation. I thought of telling him I had assigned a graduate student to arrange the chairs, or my secretary, and they had messed up. I considered at least six different possible scenarios by the time Tony stopped speaking and was waiting for my response. I said, "Tony, I messed up. I forgot to take care of the chairs." I will always remember his response: "Jerry, congratulations. You have just learned how to handle incompetence in a competent way." In other words, you have improved your whole persona by telling the truth, by taking ownership of your failure.

6. When you harm one personal quality, you simultaneously harm the others. I once had three graduating seniors in my undergraduate Love and Health class. While giving a pop quiz on honesty, I saw these three, who were friends, looking over each other's exams. I could hardly believe they were cheating on a test about honesty!

I gave all three a failing grade on the test and an F for the course. That meant none of the three would graduate that Spring. All three came to see me and swore they didn't look at each other's papers. My response was, "Before you came here today I only knew one thing about your character, that you cheat. Now I know two things: you also lie."

As you may imagine, this story grew legs. Their parents came to see me. They had planned graduation parties, with relatives coming from afar. They threatened to cause me trouble, to get me fired, and so forth, but I stood my ground. The moral of the story is this: once you decide to cheat, or in other ways compromise a principle, it is in all likelihood a decision to adopt additional undesirable behaviors that go with it.

As king of Israel, King David, in the Old Testament, had gained God's favor in so many instances that he was described as a man after God's own heart. One afternoon, David happened to walk on his balcony. From that vantage point, he watched a married woman taking a bath. Being taken by her beauty, he invited her to dinner. Bathsheba's husband, Uriah, a captain in David's army, was at that time fighting at the battlefront.

A love affair developed between David and Bathsheba that ended up in her getting pregnant. David tried a number of stratagems to hide his adulterous relationship. He called Uriah home so that people would assume Bathsheba's pregnancy was a result of her husband's furlough. But Uriah couldn't bring himself to be intimate with his wife. He felt he could not enjoy the pleasures of life at home while soldiers under his command were risking their lives fighting a war.

Finally, David sent orders to have Uriah placed at the forefront of battle. When the fighting became fierce, his fellow soldiers were to withdraw, thus assuring that Uriah would get killed. Bathsheba would then become a widow and David could marry her and all would end well. The prophet Samuel, however, took a different view and confronted the king with the truth.

The question is, How did all this begin? How did David, a man who had a heart like God's, become responsible for committing adultery and taking an innocent man's life? How could Israel's most renowned king fall so grievously from grace? But the whole episode began inadvertently, by his watching a married woman take a bath, then inviting her to dinner, and so forth, until David had compromised his own principles. The lesson to be learned from this is that personal qualities don't exist in a vacuum. They are part of a fabric of many interconnected qualities or cultivated character traits, all of which cleave together to form one's personality.

7. The locus of control must be internal. In the words of John Adams, "Those who rely on written codes of conduct are the most harmful among us." Codes must be written in our hearts for them to be of worth. I had a colleague, a health teacher, who was a chain smoker. Her refrain was, "I wish they would make cigarettes illegal so I could quit." In other words, the responsibility for her smoking wasn't hers but the nation's lawmakers! Alvin Shaw stated it his way, "The error of the ages, why so many do not

win, is seeking power without, instead of power within."

One of the great books I read in law school explained how the law helped regulate fundamental rights that are accorded all citizens. But the law cannot, and should not, attempt to regulate the higher aspects of human life. These can be governed effectively only by the individual. One secret of the success of a free society is that it works because most people freely elect to live a life agreeable with humanity's higher values. When they fail to live up to these ideals, society cannot long sustain itself.

8. You can almost always reverse the harm done to personal qualities. One of the most pernicious thoughts people can have is to give up trying because you made a mistake or didn't perform up to expectations. Because developing good qualities takes practice, the same as with other human skills, we should allow for errors along the way. No one starts with his personality fully perfected. When you see someone at the "top of the mount" in developing character, you can assume he didn't fall there.

A number of years ago, I interviewed football coaches to fill the vacant head coach position at our university. One of the applicants had been the assistant coach for many years and assumed the position would be conferred upon him. When it became evident this might not happen, he became agitated and said, "But I have fifteen years' experience coaching football." I responded, "I disagree. I think you have one year's experience repeated fifteen times." If we want to improve our work, or ourselves, we must learn from our mistakes or we will continue repeating them over and over.

I once worked with a colleague who was single. She was dating a young man with whom she had established a serious relationship. When pressed for a commitment, the man revealed he was married and the father of two. As she described this to me, she explained how this had happened to her three times in a row. She would go with a man and become serious, only to discover he was married and had children.

When I asked her where she met them, she said, "In bars." (I'm sure you've heard the question, What do all men in singles' bars have in common? They're all married.) At some point in our conversation she asked, "Then where do I meet eligible single men?" I asked her to give me time and I would think about it.

I finally suggested she buy a few shares of stock, attend a stockholders' meeting, and see who else was there. She did. She bought two shares of stock in a nationally recognized company with impressive credentials. She attended a stockholders' meeting and met a single vice-president. They're now happily married.

Insanity is sometimes defined as repeating the same behaviors and expecting different results. If things are not going well, take a look at the twelve ingredients of health and see which ones require work or which mistakes you're repeating over and over. Ninety percent of the time this will suggest the needed changes.

9. The longer you wait to start your reversal of hurtful habits, the more difficult it gets. Bad habits are as hard to break as good ones. We all know people who smoke cigarettes, drink too much, do drugs, overeat, justify inappropriate behaviors, and so forth. We see where their actions lead. We don't have to wait for the younger generation to grow old in order to observe how such lives will end in unhappiness and disease. Because the longer you put off changing destructive behavior the harder it gets, you must address the issue immediately. This leads to my last guideline.

10. The tenth, and possibly most important, principle was written many years ago by Henry Wadsworth Longfellow: "You cannot run away from weakness. You must at some point fight it out and either win or perish. And if that be so, why not now, and where you stand?"

As a sophomore in college, I smoked cigarettes and drank beer, though I knew both were inappropriate for me. As was my habit, I memorized quotes while walking to class. The day I memorized the quote from Longfellow, his words spoke directly to my heart: "You can't run away from weakness. . . ." I had wanted to stop smoking and drinking at some point, so there and then I took out my pack of cigarettes and threw it in the trash. From that day on, I have never smoked another cigarette or drunk an alcoholic beverage. In short, "If not now, when?" I believe it was Stephen Covey who said, "All victories are internal before they can be external."

STANZAS ON FREEDOM

Men! Whose boast it is that ye
    Come of fathers brave and free
If there breathe on earth a slave,
    Are ye truly free and brave?

If ye do not feel the chain,
    When it works a brother's pain,
Are ye not base slaves indeed.
    Slaves unworthy to be free?

Women! Who shall one day bear,
    Sons to breathe New England air.
If ye hear without a blush,
    Deeds that make the roused blood
    rush,

Like red lava through your veins,
    For your sisters now in chains –
Answer! Are ye fit to be
    Mothers of the brave and free?

Is true Freedom but to break,
    Fetters for our own dear sake?
Or with heart and hand to be,
    Earnest to make others free?

They are slaves who fear to speak
    For the fallen and the weak;
They are slaves who will not choose
    Hatred, scoffing and abuse,

Rather than in silence shrink,
    From the truth they needs must think;
They are slaves who dare not be
    In the right with but two or three.

James Russell Lowell -

6

Many people owe the grandeur of their lives to tremendous difficulties
—Spurgeon

Personal Metamorphosis

One discovery I made about changing self is that it works progressively—it takes place in stages. For me, change followed nearly linearly the three parts of our human makeup, physical, mental, and spiritual. I realized early in life that I was a good athlete and was therefore physically capable. Then, during my college years, I found I was just as competent mentally as I was physically. As I looked inside myself to discover who I was, I began to develop faith in what I saw. I began to trust my own judgment, insight, and ability to solve problems.

Recognizing my spiritual capacity, on the other hand, took a lot longer. The spiritual path was more elusive because the proof or results I wanted came only after the fact, so to speak. Only after I would exercise faith in a spiritual principle enough to act upon it did I observe a gradual change manifesting itself in which things "fell into place" and I attained a measure of that peace "that surpasses all understanding." Before I personally experienced this, however, had you explained to me about this process, I might have agreed with you, but I could not have known what you were talking about. It is for each of us to discover this transformation for him- or herself.

Students often asked how we find out about our spiritual side. How does a person determine his spiritual attributes, who he is, for example, and what his mission or purpose in life is intended to be? I personally found the process of self-discovery somewhat easy to grasp conceptually but often difficult, or even painful, to put in practice. It required an open mind, a constant willingness to listen, reason, believe, and ultimately to assimilate what my search for the truth would reveal. Most of all, it required the follow-up of acting upon my discoveries, sometimes finding out only by trial and error what was true and what wasn't, what worked and what didn't.

This "conversion" to the truth was not a one-time dramatic event in my life, in which everything suddenly changed for the better. It was an ever evolving process. This was the case in spite of my receiving a solid spiritual grounding in my earliest years and while serving in community and religious organizations. I have learned that enduring spiritual change does not consist in a single life-altering experience—that is, unless you want to stay in one place, unwilling to step out of your comfort zone and move forward. Rather, I have found the process of discovering the truth and applying it in my life exponential—always expanding and ever opening up new possibilities for progress and growth. However, this has happened only in proportion to my willingness to learn and to change.

Where, in fact, does one get the idea that life is static and not subject to change? If change is the one constant we know about the universe, then why should we not improve upon our circumstances? If time itself moves forward, for example, and we're not progressing with it, then aren't we actually regressing? Too many of us, in fact, have already done that and, to our dismay, seen our lives stagnate. Either way, we *will* change. It's up to us whether it will be for the better or worse.

The initial process of self-discovery that leads to change is perhaps best profiled in the Johari window concept, which says that each of us may look into four "windows" to find out more about ourselves. The first asks, What do I know about myself, and what do others know about me? The second, What do I know about myself that others don't

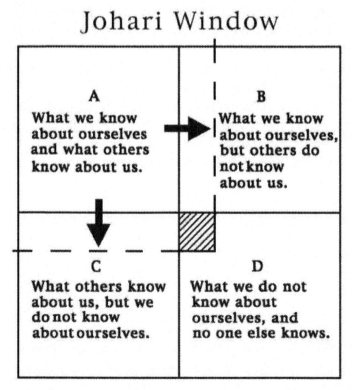

Johari Window

A	**B**
What we know about ourselves and what others know about us.	**What we know about ourselves, but others do not know about us.**
C	**D**
What others know about us, but we do not know about ourselves.	**What we do not know about ourselves, and no one else knows.**

know? The third, What do others know about me that I don't know? And the fourth, What don't I know about myself, and what don't others know about me?

Understanding our spiritual dimension requires measurable success in discovering what occurs in Window D. Many of our spiritual capacities and characteristics reside in that mysterious fourth window. This process of discovery is in turn facilitated by expanding upon what occurs in Windows B and C. In other words, by sharing more of what we know about ourselves that others don't know, and by discovering more of what others know about us that we don't know, we come to a greater self-awareness.

Focusing our attention on Windows B and C integrates our physical, mental, and spiritual natures as we gather more accurate information about who we are and what we want to achieve in life. Of course, this requires that we share with some trustworthy person personal data relating to our physical, mental, and spiritual selves. Wisdom dictates that we approach this process thoughtfully and prayerfully, divulging sensitive information only to those who will use it in a constructive way.

One of the most common statements students made about the Love and Health course was, "I learned more in this class than any other I've ever taken." Why was this? Because we sat and talked with each other. We willingly shared with one another parts of our Windows B and C, thus allowing us to peek more clearly into Window D.

A discussion we often had in class was what boys liked most and least in girls, and vice versa. Boys generally explained that what they hated most in girls was their foul mouth. You could see the stunned look on many girls in the class, one of whom said, "What do you mean by foul-mouthed?" The boys answered, "Mostly using the F word." (Actually they were more graphic) One shocked girl responded, "Are you f....... kidding? I couldn't f....... talk if I couldn't f....... say f....." She was close to being right. It was one of her first glances into her Window 3, or what others knew about her that she didn't know.

After teaching college for over forty years, two things had become clear to me. First, universities are not primarily institutions where students are taught to think or learn. Instead, they create environments for memorizing information, for gaining technical skills and getting degrees. Though they're good at dispensing these things, universities are not good at teaching students to think critically, to answer tough questions about themselves, or to help them conceptualize what life is all about. Nevertheless, in Love and Health we were able to accomplish some of this.

One day, I arrived in the classroom earlier than usual and found three nursing students already there. As it was unusual for nursing majors to take Love and Health, I asked why they had registered for this course. They responded by giving me several politically correct answers, which, in effect, told me nothing. So I said, "Tell me what have you learned in the last three months?" Each was quick to quote data upon data, studies upon studies about which they had meticulously taken notes and which they had commendably memorized. They knew the names of the scientists who had conducted the studies, the authors of books and articles, their latest research, statistics, and so forth. When at last they were convinced they had demonstrated a knowledge of everything they had learned, I said, "Those are things you've memorized. I want to know what you've *learned*." They looked at each other in nonplused silence, completely baffled.

I said, "I'm sure you've jumped through all the right hoops in this class and that each of you will probably earn an A. But in my opinion none of you has learned anything." So I offered them the following arrangement: "If the three of you will promise not to take another note in this class, if you will simply ingest all that is said and participate on a personal level, I will give each of you an A, regardless of how well you have done on your exams."

For the rest of the semester these students did just that. When the course was over, all three wrote on their evaluations that for the first time as university students they had actually learned something. It scared them to realize how much they didn't know and how little they had learned at the university—not about nursing and technical matters but about life, living, love, and healing.

The second thing that became clear to me about universities is that they're not designed, built, or conducted primarily with students' interests in mind but with those of the professors and administrators. In Love and Health, we tried to reverse that situation and create an environment conducive to learning. There is an axiom in education that states, "You can lead a horse to water, but you can't make him drink." I found that my job was not to lead the horse to water, nor to try to make him drink. It was simply to make him thirsty and then get out of the way. The horse and nature did the rest.

When we arouse thirst in a person about his physical, mental, and spiritual world, learning then begins, usually intensely. When that integration begins to congeal, to "hang together," a process of centering occurs. A person undergoing this kind of growth usually ends up being in harmony with him, or herself, with others and with nature. The person drinks from the well of truth that is accessible to each of us, and of which our spirit is the gatekeeper. When we create the conditions for the spirit to take control in our lives, truth flows through us from the divine source to which we have access. From my experience in Love and Health, and from life in general, I learned that the spirit doesn't need much tutoring, just empowering.

Allowing the truth to emanate from our spiritual core need not be something we experience only occasionally. So long as we continue to follow the spirit's direction, the truth will continue to flow through us. As soon as we relegate our guidance to a non-spiritual influence, however, we surrender control to the physical world, creating imbalance and uncenteredness, which lead to dis-ease. In short, no amount of public or private "education" can generate true learning—it must come from within. If the process of integrating our physical, mental, and spiritual dimensions is not an essential part of the equation, we will not really *learn* anything, just memorize data and master skills.

In the process of "teaching" Love and Health, if I could facilitate students to initiate this process, they would immediately begin intuitively to seek and find what they needed to know, whether I mentored them or not. And when students learned things, I too learned by observing and participating in the process. That is what the course on Love and Health ended up teaching me. As for love, I realized I could not teach this, but I could help make students thirsty for learning about love. After accomplishing that, we just had fun drinking at the well and experiencing the healing.

Looking into Window 4 taught me a lot about my own purpose in life. In the end, I found that facilitating the process of learning was what I enjoyed doing most. The twofold question Gary Zukav had asked—"Who are you and what do you want?"—was preeminently answered for me. Most importantly, I realized that the administrative position at the university from which I had been fired was not really what I wanted and that it wasn't the career for which I was best suited. Rather, my professional calling and great joy in life was to make students thirsty and then witness their self-discovery and healing. A great teacher, Thomas Monson, summarized this process when he counseled people to first search inward, then reach outward, and then look upward, which, in turn, would allow them to move forward.

PEACE

Each of us seeks for peace of mind and spirit, but we sometimes fear that it means giving up excitement, uniqueness and individuality. Peace sounds like contentment, which sounds like settling, conforming, letting the fire go out.

In reality, peace allows you to go more deeply into the world and consequently to experience more excitement, to be more unique and, like truth, to be independent in the sphere in which you exist.

Peace is not something you can force on anything or anyone – much less upon one's own mind and spirit. That is like trying to quiet the ocean by pressing upon the waves. Peace lies in somehow opening to reality, allowing anxiety, moving into the tumult, diving deeply in the waves, where underneath, within, peace simply is.

Peace is being whole and intact while the wayward world, all around you, dashes itself on the calm and serenity of your steadfastness and resolve. It is you, being a wholesome you. It is you being connected with, but independent of all others who have discovered peace.

It is going where you wish, yet traveling with dignity, purity and purpose. It is saying to the world, "Come, be at peace with me, yet don't fear my difference." Peace is fire to the spirit, and manna for the soul. It allows you to entrain with others, yet to soar by yourself. And like love, it is infinite and essential.

To be at peace is not to conform to truth, but to incorporate truth into who and what you are.

Adapted from writings of
Gerald May

7

The flower that follows the sun does so even on cloudy days
—Leighton

Love and Health for Graduates

A year after the undergraduate course on Love and Health was underway, I wrote a similar course for our graduate program. The main difference between the two was that the graduate version consisted of a summer institute. That meant I could use some of the students' tuition money to pay for guest speakers to participate with us in class. Two years later, this became one of the most popular courses on campus. It wasn't unusual to have a hundred graduate students take it as an elective.

During that time, I was also supervising a graduate program whose main purpose was to prepare teachers to teach School Health Education. So I made the Love and Health Institute a core part of the program. If we could teach people to love themselves, they certainly would be willing to abstain from smoking, eat a healthy diet, exercise, live disciplined, wholesome lives, and so forth. And if they understood what love was, they would surely not put someone whom they loved in harm's way or at any kind of risk. Over the next twenty-one years, that summer course remained the centerpiece of the graduate program in School Health Education.

I first taught this graduate institute in 1982. By that time, however, love and health were becoming popular national topics, the object of intense interest and research. Authors like Bernie Siegel, Joan Borysenko, Gary Zukav, Ken Pelletier, Dick and Annette Bloch, Ashley Montagu, C. Norman Shealy, Carolyn Myss, Dean Ornish, Jerry Jampolsky, and others were blazing trails with their books and workshops. Publications on the subject were proliferating, advocating the very principles I had been teaching in my two courses on Love and Health. This bonanza of excellent scholarship thus allowed me to finally use many of their materials.

In the tenth year of the graduate course—1992—I decided to conduct a symposium on love and health. I would expand my little summer institute into an international event, inviting all the speakers we had been reading from or listening to, now to address us first-hand. With the help of a few friends, I organized the International Love and Health Congress. My associate, Bernie Siegel, who was well known in this field, played a vital part in convincing all the afore-mentioned speakers to participate. To our surprise and delight, people registering for this congress came from thirteen countries and thirty-eight states.

The International Love and Health Congress—a three-day event—was an amazing success. By inviting these internationally known speakers, I had the opportunity to meet all the people I admired in this field and on whose research and writings we had feasted on in class. Because of the hundreds of people who attended, we essentially took over the campus for three days. Best of all, the university picked up the tab and my students received the rare privilege of meeting many renowned people who were experts in our field of study and in related areas of interest.

It seemed funny to me that this intense activity centered around the very course the curriculum committee had once said no one would take seriously and which the nursing department had voted against. In fact, it was a watershed moment for me personally that was itself a testimonial to the principles these speakers and I had taught, namely that spirit-initiated learning had the power to bring self-discovery, heal unhealthy conditions, reverse adversarial circumstances, and restore peace and balance in people's lives. It certainly had done so, and was continuing to do so, for me personally.

It was indeed thrilling to have such dynamic speakers and authors come to our campus and interact, through lectures and workshops, with my students and others. The synergy of so many teachers and learners associating with one another was empowering and left an indelible impression on us all. I never felt so gratified as when we met face to face and soul to soul with men and women who had devoted so much of their lives to the subject of love and its relationship to, and impact on, human health.

Of course there were the mishaps. Dick and Annette Bloch of H&R Block were asked to participate, and it took considerable effort for them to work this speaking engagement into their busy schedule. When invited to a barbeque we had arranged for participants the evening before the congress, they were gracious but had previous commitments. However, with some arm-twisting and creative travel plans, we arranged to get them to New Haven the evening of the barbeque. I promised to pick them up at their hotel and accompany them myself.

If you have ever organized or conducted such an event, you won't be surprised when I tell you that I clean forgot to pick them up. But I wasn't aware of my mistake until the next day, the first day of the congress. As we took a break between talks, I noticed an attractive, well-dressed woman walking rather rapidly down the aisle towards me. It was Annette Bloch. Even then, my oversight still hadn't occurred to me. After all the adjustments they had made in their schedule to attend the barbecue, I hadn't shown up. Both had dressed for the occasion and had waited in their hotel room for over an hour. (Cell phones were invented too late to save this situation.)

When she came about two feet from me, she started to rehearse how I had stood them up. Only then did I realize my error. She was very graphic about how my faux pas had made them feel and I felt as though I were being disciplined by my dad all over again. When her husband finally showed up, he took a little pleasure in my pain and then said to his wife, "Do you think he's been punished enough, dear?" She said, "Yes," then reached out with both arms and gave me a hug. What a lesson she taught in resolving conflict! Go to the person who has offended you, tell him exactly how you feel, then hug him. What a lesson in love, to say nothing of graciousness! To this day, we remember this incident in good humor. It seems I was the only host who had ever treated them like that.

I didn't know it at the time, but many administrative personnel from Griffin Health Services, a local hospital, were present at the congress. The hospital's CEO had purchased tickets for himself and any administrators who wished to attend. Because the event had been such a success, people asked when we would hold the next one. I replied that this was a one-time occasion. I had put it together with the help of a few friends and student workers and without the aid of a secretary to make phone calls, travel plans, or financial arrangements. I had no desire to go through such harrowing preparations again.

Griffin's CEO came to me, however, and explained that his hospital would be interested in co-sponsoring a second congress. Would I run it again? He promised the kind of support that wasn't always forthcoming from the university. So the following summer my university and his hospital jointly sponsored and conducted the Second International Love and Health Congress. Once again it was a success and we almost doubled the number of attendees.

At the conclusion of this congress, the CEO of the hospital again asked to speak with me. He requested that I join his hospital staff and share the concepts I was teaching in my Love and Health course with his 1,200 employees. I replied, "I'm a university professor. We don't know how to *do* anything, we just suggest things." He then offered me a nice consulting fee to attempt this experiment at his hospital. I thought, "Maybe I can do this."

SELF MASTERY

What tho I conquer my enemies,
  And lay up store and pelf,
I am a conquerer poor indeed,
  Till I subdue myself.

What tho I read and learn by heart,
  Whole books while I am young,
I am a linguist in disgrace,
  Who cannot guard my tongue.

What tho on campus I excel,
  A champ in meet and fight,
If trained, efficient still I can't
  Control an appetite.

What tho exemptions write my name,
  High on the honor-roll,
Electives, solids fail me if,
  I learn no self control.

What tho I graduate and soar,
  And life is good to me,
My heart shall write me failure till,
  I learn Self Mastery.

Author Unknown

8

*Pain nourishes courage. You can't be brave if you have
only wonderful things happen to you*
—Mary Tyler Moore

The Spiritual Birth of a Hospital

The CEO of Griffin Health Services, John Bustelos, was one of the most exceptional people I have ever worked with. (He would get upset if I said, "worked for.") He had rescued a hospital about to collapse from economic woes and built a new facility that became one of the most unique healing enterprises in the country. It was so singularly successful, in fact, that hospital administrators came from all over the world to observe it in action. There was such a demand for tours of his medical facility that we finally had to limit the number of groups who could visit. Having to turn some away, we even began charging a fee for the tour. This is how it happened:

When John became CEO of Griffin in the early 1980s, not only was the hospital close to financial collapse, the level of medicine being practiced was itself suspect. A third of the local population let it be known they would not go to the hospital under any circumstances. The rest were reluctant to do so but realized it might possibly be their only hope. This hospital was seldom viewed as a place where real healing occurred. In reality, it didn't even bear any likeness to a medical facility. It looked more like a factory whose waiting room resembled a 1950s bus station.

Griffin was housed in the oldest, most rundown physical plant in the state. Serious health problems were never handled there but were always directed to other hospitals. In many respects, the kinds of medicine performed at this facility resembled what was practiced in third-world countries. Under almost any circumstances, patients were not given quality professional attention but were treated in ways that left a lot to be desired.

Much of the hospital's income was generated from expensive medical tests and treatments that Medicare and insurance companies were willing to cover but that were not always needed. Although such practices helped the hospital survive financially, they made any ethical administrator cringe when he or she went to work in the morning. Because of the overuse of diagnostic testing and similar such abuses, people's use of Griffin—or rather, their involuntary involvement in the institution once they went there—was more than double that of any other hospital in the state.

This medical facility, moreover, was located in the smallest town in the state. It served a community with the lowest average income and educational scores of any other town state-wide. It was located within forty-five minutes of ten much better hospitals. Lastly, future plans for Griffin consisted simply of "tripling the number of beds," without any motive or agenda other than to help the hospital get more patients rather than actually aiding them. As far as any game plan existed at all, the institution's philosophy was merely reactive; it was never proactive.

The only ideology the hospital followed, in fact, was to emulate, as much as possible, what other medical facilities did. No one questioned the way things were done, the way they ought to be done, or what the hospital's future might hold. The staff was unwilling to change their routine. They weren't receptive to new ways or new ideas—no one thought much about it. No one asked big organizational questions such as, "Who are we, and what is our mission?" That was the kind of medical facility John Bustelos inherited when he became CEO. Like universities, hospitals were seldom built for the benefit of patients but for the convenience of the administrators, doctors, and staff.

In 1989, under John Bustelos, the management began asking serious questions about the current and future state of the hospital. This inquiry started with the personal experiences of three of its administrators. A vice-president had a life-threatening accident and was treated at the facility. Another underwent a mastectomy under abominable conditions. And finally, the CEO himself lost his wife to complications of diabetes there. All were appalled at what they had observed firsthand among the players in their own medical arena.

The questionable procedures used and poor conditions under which patients were treated during these personal emergencies led to a new dialogue. In the light of such unprofessionalism as was displayed before their very eyes, it wasn't long before the administration concluded, "This place badly needs an overhaul." They reasoned that if theirs was the kind of treatment patients received who were a part of the institution, then how much worse must it be for those who were not a part of it?

The result of this dialogue was that the administrative cabinet began conducting retreats based on management concepts conceived by Singe and Barry. Each month, a twelfth of the hospital's staff attended seminars run by the administration. They began by presenting Window 1 to the staff: What do I know about this hospital, and what do you know about it? (See the Johari

Window Concept, Chapter 6.) That process alone took more than a year to complete. But from the staff's sharing of their perceptions with one another there emerged a clear and concise view of the hospital that was understood by all. There now existed collective agreement about both the institution's positive and negative qualities. All participants were on the same page about its successes and failures.

After completing that phase of inquiry, the management continued the retreats but now presented Windows 2 and 3. From these, they learned what the staff knew about the hospital that others didn't know. And the opposite: what others knew about the hospital that the staff didn't know. The assumption was that once this information was shared and perceived by all, greater insights would follow into Window 4. The truth of what Griffin was and what its mission was intended to be would then reveal itself.

It was during these conference sessions that the vice-president of finance explained where the hospital's income was coming from and how and where it was spent. For most participants, this was their first window into the facility's financial practices. A comment by Dorothy, a middle-level manager, was typical. When asked what she thought should be done about a fiscal problem, she broke into tears: "I've worked here for over ten years, and this is the first time anyone has asked me what I thought." From all we know about how sharing information can be remedial, was it any wonder this hospital had a reputation for not being a place of healing?

What emerged from these retreats was a clear-cut mission for Griffin. It should come as no surprise that this mission was not what outsiders said it ought to be. Nor did it reflect what other hospitals were doing. The needs of the community, not the self-serving interests of the institution, were now the topic of discussion. A long-range plan was developed to address the newly surfaced dreams and visions of the physicians and staff about how best to help the patients who came to the hospital for treatment.

At this point in Griffin's metamorphosis, about eighty percent of physicians and staff said they wanted to be a part of this dream and experience the change. The other twenty percent, who felt they could not make such a paradigm shift, and who didn't want to participate, were invited to seek employment elsewhere. This "housecleaning" of the hospital did much to promote unity among the management and staff and boosted the morale of those who remained.

The eighty percent now began to address the twofold question Peter Singe asks in his book, *The Fifth Discipline*: "Who am I and what do I want?" They determined that despite the less-than-desirable conditions under which they worked, they had the potential for being, or were already, in fact, good healthcare providers. They acknowledged that though the hospital itself was a mess, they were willing to invest time and energy to bring about positive change. They began to believe that a transformation could be accomplished in spite of the huge obstacles and challenges they faced.

These retreats thus generated a clear idea of the current state of the hospital and a commitment by those who remained to improve their circumstances. However, it would take another two years of retreats before a well-defined picture emerged of what could or should be done. As a part of the institution's search for this new vision, a vice-president was assigned to look for a model of healthcare that reflected what physicians and staff wanted to implement at Griffin. This would be something unique as no conventional model seemed to fit the staff's unanimously approved goals.

An intensive search revealed a model called Planetree, which advocated patient-centered healthcare. This concept was so persuasive and comprehensive, it even included the design and construction of hospital buildings along with articulate suggestions for the institution's internal organization and management. At last, a model was found that matched the dreams and visions of Griffin's administration and staff!

At that time, however, it was common for smaller hospitals and other modest companies, especially those in financial distress, to be bought out by larger ones. The parent hospital would then make cosmetic changes to the minor one and sell it for a profit. But after that happened, the medical facility would often end up in a worse state than before. Its problems would simply be perpetuated under a facade of improvement.

In fact, John Bustelos was approached frequently to sell off Griffin and was offered handsome stipends in return. Instead, he chose to follow his dream. He and many of his associates had by now caught the vision of what could be achieved. They were convinced they could create a place where real healing could occur, an environment conducive to effective medical treatment and to restful follow-up convalescence.

But such a challenge wouldn't be easy. For all practical purposes, Griffin was broke. It had just lost a lawsuit that left it unable to obtain insurance. Members of the board who saw their "ox gored" complained and threatened the hospital's management. These conditions made it difficult to implement the needed changes. State regulatory agencies were reluctant to approve a new plant, to say nothing of getting an untested and unproven Planetree type of facility funded and insured.

To make a long story short, Griffin's management created its own offshore insurance company. A hospital was designed that fully conformed to the

Planetree model. The administration then somehow obtained the funding and built the new hospital. This facility, from start to finish, was built around the needs of patients. To give you an idea of what was incorporated into its design, I mention just a few of its features:

A kitchen was provided on each floor in which patients who were capable were encouraged to prepare the kinds of foods they preferred. Volunteers came in daily at scheduled times to bake homemade bread or cookies for both patients and visitors. The smell of the hospital was thus not of an institution but of a hospitable home.

Instead of the impersonal tile and linoleum that had covered the previous facility's floors, all floors were now carpeted. Quiet prevailed throughout the hospital. No clicking of heels of people traipsing down the halls was heard that could disturb a patient's rest.

Pianos, elegant paintings, and fish tanks full of green plants and colorful fish were located on every floor, providing a warm, homelike environment. Volunteers regularly played pianos and other musical instruments in all parts of the hospital.

The birthing center had queen-size beds so that dads could feel welcome to stay over. At the time we proposed to provide these accommodations, we discovered that no such hospital beds existed. They had to be specially made for Griffin.

Ample storage space in every building ensured that medical equipment never needed to be left standing around to clutter up rooms and hallways.

Special cubicles called Care Partner Rooms sported foldout beds, TVs, closets, and showers for spouses, relatives, or partners who wished to stay in patients' rooms. Such persons could then help with their loved ones' care. This same concept of domestic assistance, however, was encouraged in every part of the hospital, even where Care Partner Rooms didn't exist.

A hospital library provided access to medical data about patients' illnesses or diseases. In fact, every patient was furnished an information packet from the library that included highlighted references to his or her particular condition. Additionally, patients had complete access to charts and files covering their medical care.

These and many other innovations in healthcare characterized the new facility. Once construction based on the Planetree model was completed, and once the necessary training and medical philosophy had been implemented, something of a miracle happened. Griffin was transformed from a warehouse for sick people into a venue for healing, a spiritual Mecca, a beacon of light for all who dreamed of a healthcare Camelot. It wasn't unusual for patients and visitors to make such comments as, "I felt more as if I were in a hotel than in a hospital." "I sensed a spirit of healing the moment I walked in the door." "I received love from everyone I encountered there."

We thus discovered that it was indeed possible to create such a unique healing facility when we addressed the physical, mental, and spiritual needs of both patients and those who administered their care. I once asked John when he thought this transformation actually started. He replied, "It began the moment Griffin's staff started to feel love for one another at the retreats." There, they shared their dreams, fears, doubts, and innermost feelings about all parts of the Johari Window. From their loving relationships with one another a miracle was born.

The success of this medical creation led to a flood of praise and endorsements from well-known people. From cardiologist Dr. Steven Sinatra came this comment: "To John Bustelos…an innovator in complementary cardiology: your leading-edge programs on alternative cardiology care are perhaps the best in the country." From Elliott Dascher: "You have created a healing place that is palpable the minute you walk in the front door." And from Peter Singe: "One of the most successful sustainable experiments in the U.S."

That was the developing organization John Bustelos had now asked me to join. My job would be to help teach the process of promoting love and spiritual well-being to the hospital's management and staff. As best as I can recall, this was the charge he gave me when I began work at Griffin. He wanted me to implement programs that would promote love as an integral part of its entire operation. Because the administration had developed a long-range plan calling for a spiritual dimension to every decision that would be made, someone had to figure out how this was to be accomplished. That someone was me.

I'm not sure that either John or I understood precisely all that would be involved in integrating love and spirituality into the organization and running of such a large institution. We were traveling where neither of us had been before. And as far as we could determine, no one else had been there before either. Because of this uncertainty, John wanted me to be a part of decisions that he made personally as well as those he made administratively. I therefore also served as his spiritual advisor and mentor.

It was with an attitude of "No miracle is impossible" that John and I flew to the West Coast to speak directly with the parent organization of Planetree. Because Planetree had experienced differences and difficulties in its leadership, an actual working model of its philosophy wasn't readily available. When other hospitals contacted Planetree for a description of what its organization was all about, they were usually sent to us. Griffin thus began serving as an example or practical model of Planetree's ideology that people could observe firsthand and choose to emulate.

After John and I visited Planetree, just as we were leaving its headquarters, I turned to him and said, "You know, we should just take over Planetree and eliminate the middle man." Two years later, that is what we did—Planetree became a part of Griffin's organization.

As John Bustelos' hospital experience both predated and coincided with mine, I have asked him to describe Griffin's history and transformation in his own words in the following chapter.

From THE PROPHET

No man can reveal to you aught but that which lies half asleep in the dawning of your knowledge.

The teacher who walks in the shadow of the temple, among his followers, gives not of his wisdom but rather of his faith and lovingness.

If he is indeed wise he does not bid you enter the house of his wisdom, but rather leads you to the threshold of your own mind.
Kahlil Gibran

9

Beginning the Griffin Experience

by John Bustelos

As I'm sure you are finding out, the story Jerry Ainsworth tells in this book is one of insight and courage. His tale is the whisper of the heart of a man who exhibits compassion and generosity, wisdom and intelligence. It is this spirit in him that makes him such a dear friend and moves me to add my brief chronicle.

My friendship with Jerry developed over a decade during which he and I were deeply involved in one the most difficult of all human endeavors, that of changing the mental modality that determines how people see what they see, hear what they hear, and learn what they can learn. In other words, we became well acquainted while participating with many whose lives were in the process of being profoundly altered during the complete transformation and reinvention of Griffin Health Services in Derby, Connecticut, through the 1990s.

Jerry's is the story of a life-long metamorphosis leading to his attainment of joy and fulfillment. Despite the initial resistance he experienced when embarking on life's journey, and despite the pitfalls he stumbled over along the way, his tale illustrates the profound insights and cumulative wisdom that can transform a person when the heart and spirit have the courage to press on at a time when it would have been much easier to just quit. Because Jerry didn't detour from his life's purpose once he found it, his readers will benefit greatly from his story.

His helpful discoveries and innovations are what this book is all about. Not only is love an essential ingredient in our enjoyment of good health, but it is within a holistic framework of the physical, mental, emotional, and spiritual dimensions of love that we create the conditions of joy, fulfillment, and purpose in life that each of us seeks, whether we seek these consciously or unconsciously.

Jerry's advancement of these concepts at an International Congress on Love and Health held in August 1992 led to our first meeting. His subsequent involvement in Griffin Health Services, where I served as President and CEO, cemented our continuing friendship.

At the time I met Jerry, most hospital CEOs in the U.S. would not have been found near a college campus with a few hundred students looking for continuing education credits, attending a program professing a relationship between love and health. Rather, they would have been closeted with their chief financial officers and accountants looking for ways to "maximize reimbursements," deciding if it was time to form a "strategic alliance" with a larger institution or a competing hospital, or wondering if there was sufficient money in the budget to acquire some new technology that just might allow their hospital to regain a market share or at least stem the tide of declining admissions that had been accelerating the past four years. Indeed, a connection between love and health would have been the last thing on their minds.

As for hospitals contemplating gaining a market share by offering alternative healthcare, such a concept gained no impetus at all until David Eisenberg's seminal article, "Unconventional Medicine in the United States," appeared in the New England Journal of Medicine in January, 1993. Even then, medical strategies based on that idea took many years to catch on.

For a number of different reasons, however, my mind was on things other than conventional ones at that time. Somehow, strange to say, love and health was what I wanted to hear about more than any other message I could have encountered.

In June of 1992, I had cut short a trip to London because of severe angina, for which I had already been treated three months earlier. After my first angioplasty, physicians told me that about thirty percent of such treatments failed. If it did in my case, then I could simply repeat it.

So there I was in London with my wife, Joan, realizing that I would probably again have to undergo that painful and scary procedure. While I resisted this conclusion for as long as I could, it became clear after a couple of Trans-Atlantic phone calls to my physician that I would nevertheless be returning home for a second angioplasty.

Though my physician tried to reassure me by saying that if my symptoms became too severe I could always turn myself in to a London hospital for emergency care, I didn't find his words comforting. By now, I just wanted to be home, though I wasn't looking forward to a long flight full of discomfort, or worse, wondering how things would be if I had a heart attack on the plane.

Nevertheless, I made it back to the U.S. without major incident. I underwent a second painful procedure and was once again reassured that if it didn't "take" this time then I could repeat it yet again. Once more, the words that were supposed to comfort me did not. In fact, this continuing "reassurance" from my physician was beginning to anger me.

Throughout my ordeal with angina and the two angioplasties, I had felt more and more as if my inner self was being disembodied. Were my physicians and I to just sit dispassionately on the sidelines while my body was poked, prodded, and repaired with only a seventy percent chance of improvement that this foremost treatment available could provide? Was that the best the medical profession could do?

Welling up inside me was the notion that I didn't like this uncertain feeling. My concerns, fears, needs, and expectations were for some reason not even a part of my conversations with my physicians. If they were, I received the distinct impression that that part of the dialogue didn't interest them nearly as much as it did me. I thus felt belittled and demeaned and hollow to my core.

Also gnawing at me was the fact that I was the CEO of a hospital that was in the throes of a major transformation. From being an organization in which institutional, provider, and employee prerogatives in almost every instance trumped those of patients, we had embarked on becoming an organization that was completely committed to putting patients first. In 1989, we had determined to distinguish our hospital as a place that would focus above all on the needs of consumers and families. We would become a national model for other hospitals by providing the kind of service only a community hospital like ours could provide.

While "patient-centered healthcare" and "patient-focused care" were just emerging as buzzwords in hospital literature, they were at that time still just marketing ploys, not full-fledged strategies. Real patient-centered care meant that patients played an active and informed role in the care they received. To that end, we were at that time building a new facility and training our healthcare staff on the Planetree model.

As an integral part of this model, we were building the most comprehensive consumer resource library possible. It would provide any medical information patients or physicians needed, from the simplest layman's explanations to the most complex journalistic articles that informed physicians about the latest research.

The Planetree model also suggested changing the concept of visiting hours from strict adherence to specific times to encouraging family members or loved ones to stay on with patients at the hospital. These could thus act as forceful advocates for patients, empowering them to be as much in charge of their convalescence as they would be comfortable with.

But what kind of example would I be setting for this positive transformation if I myself continued simply to put up with my disembodied hollowness and be treated for angina in the manner I had been? It was indeed time for me to quit gnawing at the issue and take charge of how I wanted my own health managed.

This turn of mind led me to take a crash course in the treatment of heart disease in the U.S. in the early 1990s. For the most part, I didn't like what I found. Everywhere I turned, the traditional recommended treatment seemed to be more of the same: lots of drugs, lots of tests, and then wait and see if an angioplasty would keep clogged cardiac arteries open.

About that time, I began discovering books and articles describing behavioral approaches to heart disease by Pritikin, Duke, Cooper, and Ornish. I somehow learned that Dean Ornish was actually going to be in the area at Southern Connecticut State University in New Haven. That was how I came to attend Jerry's Love and Health Congress. I went to hear Dean Ornish describe his innovative research and came away committed to finding out what it would take to get involved in his program.

Just as importantly, I was struck by Jerry's own presentation on Love and Health, the same one he details so comprehensively in this book. His easily understood discussion of the integrity of the body, mind, and spirit provided a language for me to understand why Griffin's commitment to patient-centered care was so compelling.

Many of us at Griffin had become aware of the institutional barriers that blocked our way if we wanted to live up to our commitment. Concepts aired at the congress expressed something buried deep in my subconscious about why I had become involved in healthcare administration twenty years earlier. I say "buried deeply" because everything I had learned in graduate school and later on the job had, in fact, forced my inmost feelings far from my consciousness by the sheer necessity of having to succeed and survive in my chosen field.

Jerry's eloquent presentation, together with those of speakers like Joan Borysenko, Norm Shealey, Bernie Siegel, Carolyn Myss, Gary Zukav, and others made me realize that if Griffin was going to deliver on its promise, then the integration of the body, mind, and spirit needed to be accessible to a far larger group of Griffin's employees than just the few of us who had attended the congress.

This conclusion I had come to led me to meet Jerry in person to discuss how Griffin might co-sponsor a second Love and Health Congress the following year. As you will see from Jerry's account, however, he wasn't keen on the idea at the time. It was also during these conversations that I discovered Jerry to be an ordained minister in his church.

In 1989, when Griffin's administrative cabinet had decided to drastically alter our model of healthcare, we were actually stumbling over our own words. We were, in fact, looking for a process that would provide compassion, dignity, and "wholeness" to patients by addressing all their needs. Such a process would have to deal with the body, mind, and that part of us called the spirit or "soul," a subject about which some grow nervous when it is even mentioned.

From about 1983, two years after I arrived at Griffin, the hospital had employed two full-time chaplains who had transferred from positions in Roman Catholic hospitals where full-time chaplaincies were routine. But due to illness and retirement, we would soon be without any chaplains at all. Over time, moreover, it had become clear to us that the spiritual needs of a 200-bed hospital, with a busy emergency room and 1,200 employees, could not possibly be met by two chaplains if the model under which chaplains operated remained the same. That was doubly true if we were going to provide greater attention to the combined needs of patients and staff under our new model of healthcare.

The very time we had begun searching for new chaplains was when I met Jerry. But we were also asking candidates how they might restructure the chaplain's role so that the spiritual needs of patients could be met largely through the staff. As things were, chaplains simply scheduled their hours to visit each patient once a day while additionally being available for emergencies. Unfortunately, few of the candidates we had asked even understood our question, and none of them offered an intelligent answer.

In his fish tank diagram (see Chapter 13), Jerry gives an example of why prospective chaplains were having difficulty with the question. They were trained to address the religious needs of patients individually, at scheduled times. What I was asking, on the other hand, was how to create a system in which all of Griffin's employees could assist in ministering to the spiritual needs of all patients at all times.

Answering that question, however, would require moving from the traditional orientation of a chaplain as the provider of a single service to creating an entirely new system in which the service would be provided by whoever was present whenever a need became apparent. But creating new systems and educating people other than chaplains in how to attend to the spiritual needs of patients was not a part of the training of chaplains.

Though Jerry was an ordained clergyman, he had not been trained in a divinity school. Rather, he had gained his competency through the hands-on experience that made his church of lay ministers one of the fastest-growing in the U.S. Given my unpromising encounters interviewing traditionally trained chaplains, it occurred to me that Jerry, with his completely different spiritual orientation, might be just the person to work with us as we attempted to meet the spiritual needs of all our patients.

I therefore hired Jerry as an interim chaplain and a consultant who would help us define a role for future chaplains whom we would subsequently again endeavor to employ. Because Jerry describes some of his experiences as chaplain in this book, I won't go into detail about how successful our experiment turned out. What had attracted me to co-sponsor a second Love and Health Congress with Jerry was the value I had gained from comparing what we were trying to do at Griffin with the process of integrating the body, mind, emotions, and spirit in a practical modality, as distinct from the traditional allopathic medicine in which all of us at Griffin had been immersed during our health-care careers.

From 1987, we had started using the principles of a "learning organization" articulated by Peter Singe in his book, *The Fifth Discipline*, to facilitate Griffin's transformation. Though Peter's book had not yet been published, he was teaching these principles in workshops called "Leadership and Mastery." A key discipline in Peter's training was understanding systems dynamics—how and why systems operate the way they do.

It was indeed memorable to hear Peter describe how to find a "leverage point," which, if brought into focus, could change a whole system. He would say things like, "The most effective leverage point is far removed in time and space from where the problem lies. And one of the greatest leverage points lies in what we think." In other words, organizational change involves first identifying ways of thinking that we simply accept but don't talk much about.

Jerry's integrated model was a new way of looking at health in a fundamental way. Could this provide the leverage point that would propel Griffin to become a real healing organization? That would be leverage indeed!

In fact, Jerry's became the model by which our minds were opened to new possibilities about what constitutes health—how to restore it, how to enhance it, how to talk meaningfully about it to consumer and provider alike. It also made clear that real "healing," or the restoration of health, can be accomplished even at those times when a cure is not possible and death may soon follow.

I therefore unequivocally recommend Jerry's narrative as a courageous and revealing story of personal transformation, and as an original and provocative approach to health. At the same time, his story is consistent with the expressed or felt needs each of us has when we are ill or when we seek to support a loved one in his or her healing process.

The only caution I have about Jerry's account of the events at Griffin is the impression he gives that I was responsible for all that successfully transpired between 1981 and 1998. That is not the case. All the members of the administrative cabinet, the physicians, board, and mid-level management were critical to Griffin's transformation. I'm sure that when the whole story is told, their individual and collective roles will more fully emerge.

HONESTY – TRUST – FREEDOM

Adapted from *Love is a Hunger* by Earnest Larsen

Honesty –
is the conscious effort to eliminate games from my life and therefore from the relationships in which I am involved.

Trust –
is the certitude that the other person
not only will not hurt me, but is actively involved in
the growth which I have chosen for myself.

Relationship Freedom –
Only those individuals who have chosen to lean,
without losing their individuality, can participate in loving relationships.

Quality Relationship Communication –
Indicates passing through the point of pain, to deeper understanding.

10

There is no right way to do a wrong thing
—author unknown

Organizational Metamorphosis

Though I had joined the hospital staff as a consultant, for all practical purposes I was a full-time employee. Then, just as I was getting my feet on the ground, figuring out what I was supposed to do, Griffin's two chaplains retired. So John appointed me as a new chaplain. That part of my job involved reconstituting the chaplaincy and hiring an additional chaplain.

I was as shocked by his appointment of me as were the local ministers. I belong to a church that has a lay clergy, and I therefore had no formal training in the ministry. That was not an issue for me personally, as I was already comfortable with my spiritual training and skills. Nevertheless, it was difficult for some local ministers to accept. Not only that, the very idea of my working at the hospital and influencing everything with love was a new and novel idea for physicians, nurses, and all the staff, including chaplains.

Because a part of my charge was to infuse love and spirituality into all facets of the hospital, John and I decided I would begin weekly administrative cabinet meetings with a spiritual message—a thought, prayer, story, poem, or quote. In the process, I became a de facto member of the cabinet.

After providing these spiritual preludes to cabinet discussions for about a month, I came up with another idea. I said to John, "As our goal is to help everyone at the hospital become more spiritual, especially in their work efforts, why not ask cabinet members to take turns providing the spiritual moment at the start of our meetings?" John thought it a good idea and suggested I propose this at the next cabinet discussion.

When I offered this suggestion to the members of the cabinet, there was dead silence—a prolonged silence. Finally, one of the vice-presidents said, "That's the dumbest idea I've ever heard. I came to this hospital to be in charge of quality control, not to give prayers or poems." Another silence. A second vice-president then said essentially the same thing. Two more vice-presidents followed with similar responses. I could tell this wasn't going to be easy.

Suffice to say that my new idea took considerable persuasion and adjustment. Four years later, however, these same vice-presidents were themselves suggesting inspirational thoughts, participating in meditations, yoga, and so forth, along with the rest of us.

We started the same policy at our management meetings. We would begin with a spiritual moment, which was my responsibility. Some participants liked this, or at least acted as if they did, while others hated it. Some would sit with their arms folded and glare at me with a scolding look in their eyes.

My first spiritual message to the management team went something like this: One of the goals of this hospital is the spiritual health of both employees and patients. In the words of Riddell, "Self-preservation is the first law of nature, the natural person. The preservation of others is the first law of the spirit and the spiritual person. The natural person is self-centered and egoistic. The spiritual person is centered in others and is altruistic. In the natural person, the centripetal forces exceed the centrifugal. In the spiritual person the opposite is true. Therefore, the natural person gathers to himself, while the spiritual person gives of himself to others." To the degree that we observe these principles at this hospital, it will become a more spiritual place.

The tricky part of my job, however, was that John didn't restrict his requests for spiritual thoughts to the beginning of the meetings. At any given moment during a discussion, he might stop and say, "Jerry give us some spiritual words of wisdom or insight into this issue." That would keep me on my toes. But I was fortunate that during my whole life I had memorized little quotes, poems, short stories, and so forth. And when I had to come up with a spiritual thought, I usually had something tucked away in my head or shirt pocket.

We were once in a meeting soon after a vice-president had severely reprimanded a couple of staff workers, reducing them to tears. John turned to me and said, "Jerry, any words of wisdom?" I used the following quote, "Never cut what you can untie." Everyone understood. That was the last time this vice-president was caustic to an employee, at least in front of me.

I never actually envisioned my job lasting very long. It was filled with all kinds of booby traps. Not only was I to help implement love and spirituality at the hospital, but because I had taught holistic health for years I became a part of the effort to implement alternative health modalities at Griffin as well. Meanwhile, my friends were betting I would last only a few months. And I wasn't sure I would survive very long either.

Our board of directors was often divided, and at such times meetings would become strained. After some tense moments in a meeting we had in Montreal, the board reached a compromise, something all could live with. Still, even after making this accommodation, each side remained suspicious of the other. At that point, John turned to me and asked, "Jerry, any final reflections?"

I responded with a story from Woody Allen. Someone asked him if he thought the day would come when the lion would lie down with the lamb, as predicted by the ancient prophet Isaiah. Woody responded with, "Yes, I believe the lion will ultimately lie down with the lamb. But that lamb ain't gonna get much sleep." They all got the point.

When groups of visiting hospital administrators came to Griffin, part of the tour we provided included lunch with members of our cabinet, at which the groups could ask questions. John would introduce us as we sat around the table: "This is the vice-president of finance," and so forth. When he came to me, he would say, "This is Dr. Ainsworth. He's our coordinator of spiritual enrichment." Members of the visiting group would then look at each other, confused, and ask, "What is that?" John would answer something like, "Jerry's in charge of the spiritual development of our hospital. Do something spiritual for them, Jerry. . ."

We came up with the title of Coordinator of Spiritual Enrichment for me when we hired another hospital chaplain and had to distinguish our two roles. I'm not sure we ever explained exactly what the title meant, though both John and I understood my mission. While we were interviewing potential chaplains, I explained to a candidate what my duties were relative to the CEO and in providing spiritual counsel and input at all decision-making levels. The candidate said, "You don't want a chaplain. You want a Prophet."

One program we started was to pop up a brief spiritual message on everyone's computer monitor when they turned it on in the morning. Appendices A and B contain most of the quotes I used over a period of four years. I hope you will use these in your own work environment as an inspiring way to start or sustain your day.

Every year, in its effort to raise money, Griffin raffled off a new automobile. I would dutifully purchase ten tickets for the cause. I regarded this more as an obligatory contribution than a chance of actually winning a car, especially as I had never won anything in my life. The winning ticket was always drawn during the intermission at the Christmas concert we held on a December Sunday at the local high school.

Late on Sunday afternoon, the day of the concert, just I was getting ready to leave home, John called and said, "Jerry, before the concert begins I want you to say a few words about the spirit of giving." I said, "Thanks for allowing me this ample time to prepare!"

I quickly rounded up a few books on the subject. As was my habit, I also offered a prayer for help in preparing my remarks. In the middle of my prayer, a little voice whispered to me, "You're going to win that car tonight." As I have for years trusted that little voice, I said, "Great!" Then the voice came again, "But you can't keep the car. Because your assignment is to teach the spirit of giving, you will give it away." Great! The only time I win anything, and I'm not supposed to keep it?

> ### THE HUMAN TOUCH
>
> T'is the human touch in this world that counts,
> the touch of your hand in mine.
>
> That means much more to the fainting heart,
> more than shelter, or bread or wine.
>
> For shelter is gone when the night is o're,
> and bread only lasts a day.
>
> But the touch of the hand and the sound of the voice,
> sing on in the soul alway.
>
> David Tree

I prepared a few remarks and a little poem and went to the concert. I tried to tell John I was going to win the car but he was too busy to pay attention. I told a few other cabinet members, but they responded with, "Yeah, everyone says the same thing." So I finally stopped trying to convince people and just waited for the concert to begin.

At the start of the program, as requested, I said a few words and quoted a poem by David Tree and then sat down to enjoy the concert. At intermission, John and the chairman of the board hauled a big cage on stage filled with raffle tickets. Bob reached into it, drew a ticket at random, and gave it to John. John turned pale, then read the name—my name!

I stood up and explained that I couldn't accept the car as there was someone in the audience who needed one more than I. I suggested they draw another ticket. As they did so, I thought to myself, Please don't let the winner be another doctor! Doctors had won this raffle in the past. The winner turned out to be a father of five who had a car on its last legs. He really needed the car, just as the little voice had directed.

After the concert, a nurse or two said, "Jerry, if you were going to give the car away, we could have worked something out." An interesting comment to a chaplain! Others said the whole thing was rigged by the administration. Not everyone got the message, but the message was clearly there to learn: listen to the little voice and it will direct you how to teach the spirit of giving, which was my assignment.

After that incident, I won the next two hospital raffles I participated in, which I also gave away. By now, people were asking what my secret was. I came up with this explanation: "If you're willing to give away everything you win, without hesitation, then you can win a raffle. But you have to be willing to give it up completely and without any regrets." Not many people appreciated that answer.

It wasn't enough that the hospital had now been successfully built and was running well. There were new mountains to climb, new dreams to fulfill. Prior to that, John had developed heart disease and was having angioplasty treatments. Once again, this health crisis became a learning experience. We explored different methods of treating heart disease and visited various medical centers. Dean Ornish's program of heart disease reversal in San Francisco, California, soon became the main focus of our interest. So we sent a group of hospital medical and administrative personnel to study the program.

After months of laborious negotiations, we instituted our own program of heart disease reversal at Griffin. This program was based on the research Dr. Ornish conducted that supported concepts and regimens initiated by Nathan Pritikin many years earlier in Santa Barbara, California.

The philosophy behind this new treatment rejected the belief that heart disease can't be reversed, which was something most of us had been taught in graduate school. We modified Dr. Ornish's program to include five different strategies: 1. a low-fat diet, which, in Dr. Ornish's program, consisted of less than ten percent fat and a vegetarian diet; 2. regular sustained cardiovascular exercise; 3. yoga and meditation; 4. a group process requiring the sharing of feelings; and 5. the incorporation of a spiritual component in all parts of the treatment.

In connection with the fifth strategy, we chose love and peace. We believed that to the degree we could incorporate love and peace into our lives, they would influence the reversal process as much as the four other strategies combined. As I had to come up with a spiritual theme that would reinforce the healing process. What was ultimately accepted by the hospital went something like this:

No Love, No Peace.
Know Love, Know Peace,

There was always a humorous side to these new programs. As a part of our heart disease reversal program, we originally set up a small exercise room. But as plans for new facilities continued to be discussed, the idea of a complete physical health facility emerged. At a management meeting John asked members what they thought about the hospital building a health promotion facility, with an exercise gym being a central part. After getting little response, he asked one of the managers, who responded with, "I'd rather eat bark in New Jersey and die than to join a fitness center."

There were the lighter, if not more truthful moments. As the hospital organization continued to grow and change, we would periodically create a new department. This was always done under the auspices of the Planetree model and philosophy. We also tried to incorporate meaningful elements of love and spirituality.

Once, as we met to plan one of these departments, I was asked to begin the cabinet meeting with a spiritual moment appropriate to this new beginning. I shared the following adapted statement from James Freeman Clark: "All the strength and force of people come from their faith in things unseen. Those who believe are strong. Those who doubt are weak. Strong convictions precede great actions. The person strongly possessed of an idea is the master of all who are uncertain and wavering. Clear, deep, and living convictions rule the world."

I ended my remarks with, "It's no accident that we meet to plan the birth of this new department. Many have waited and longed for its delivery. It is the culmination of faith in something not yet seen but only imagined. May we approach this prospect with awe and reverence as a midwife would when delivering a child."

When we presented our idea to the management, asking for their input, I was again asked to say a few words. I shared the following from Robert Browning:

> Truth is within ourselves; it takes no rise
> From outward things, whate're you may believe.
> There is an inmost center in us all
> Where truth abides in fullness, and "to know"
> Rather consists in opening out a way
> Whence the imprisoned splendor may escape,
> Than in effecting an entry for a light
> Supposed to be without.

Needless to say, we gave birth to a beautiful new department of which each of us felt like a proud parent.

LOVE

Love is actively communicating with others through demonstrative acts profoundly involving you in their welfare,

Such that you provide them the encouragement, sustenance, support, and stimulation they require for their unique fulfillment,

Such that they can count on you to stand by them, never committing the supreme treason of letting them down when they need you most,

Such that you are there to help them become all that is good and loving that is within their potential, which you encourage and nurture.

Ashley Montagu

11

Difficulties constitute the best education in this life
—Disraeli

Memorable Experiences as a Chaplain

As a hospital chaplain, I tried to visit every patient every day, including new-borns. I could fill a book with those experiences but a few must suffice here. Before sharing these, however, I want to make a distinction between the process of healing and that of curing. In curing, the illness or disease is remedied and ceases to exist. Healing, on the other hand, is the process of resolving the trauma caused by the disease. Thus, patients can always be healed, whether they're cured or not.

To some degree, curing is a medical and thus physical process. Healing, in the ultimate sense, is a spiritual process. As chaplain, my goal was to facilitate healing. Still, it also became evident that healing helps the process of curing the disease. At Griffin, when such a cure occurred everyone who had participated in the healing helped bring it about. As a part of the philosophy we had developed, my goal was to encourage and invite all employees to participate in our patients' healing processes.

I should add that death shouldn't necessarily be viewed as failure. Everyone dies at some point. It is the quality of life that is primary, not the quantity. Spiritual healing adds to the quality of life. In fact, as odd as it may sound, a person can die in a healthy manner. I have seen this happen many times.

As a health educator, I often saw college teachers draw a continuum on the board, with ultimate health at one end and death at the other. It took me several years to figure out that this was incorrect. Death is as normal as life, and the only solution to either is to make the most of both. The continuum should instead consist of optimal health at one end and a premature or unhealthy death at the other.

Now to share with you some of my experiences as a chaplain: I was in a patient's room one afternoon. The woman had asked if I would pray for her as she would shortly have surgery. I closed the door and began to pray. Moments into the prayer, the door flew open. It was the surgeon. He said, "Jerry, I apologize. I didn't know you were here." I said, "No problem. We were actually praying for you. Do you want to stay and listen to the rest of the prayer?" He did. I had learned that the words we utter in the presence of patients, whether in prayer or simply in conversations, can have a big impact at these critical junctures in their lives. The added presence of the surgeon who would perform the operation did much for both surgeon and patient.

The same thing was true for patients who were unconscious. I learned that even these were frequently aware of what was going on around them, though they were unable to say or do anything. On one occasion, I visited the room of a comatose patient. Her son was holding a vigil by her side and asked if I would mind saying a prayer for his mother. I did. In fact, I did so daily for a week.

During the second week, the woman came out of her coma. When I visited her again, her son being present, she said, "Jerry, will you pray for me? I heard every word you said in your previous prayers." This can be a lesson for those who visit loved ones who are unconscious. Be careful what you say in their presence. Chances are, they can hear you. Remember, only the brain is unconscious, not the mind, nor the spirit.

This was also good advice for our healthcare providers, for the doctors and nurses. We asked them not to make negative statements in the presence of unconscious or anesthetized patients that might deprive them of hope. They could be listening. Such comments could convince them to fear the future and thus stop struggling. The fact is that no matter how serious an illness, someone in the past has survived it. There is always hope. For some conditions, it may be slight indeed. But having hope is always legitimate. No one should rob a patient of hope by making negative comments.

One day, while making my rounds, I visited Natalie, a patient with pancreatic cancer. I had spoken with two of her children, who told me Natalie had lived a dissipated life. They weren't surprised she had contracted cancer. She drank a lot, smoked a lot, and had had running battles with her children over such issues for years.

When I walked into Natalie's room, I noticed she had a Bible on her lap. She immediately asked if I would read to her. She said she had been reading the Bible daily. She had left off in the fifth chapter of Daniel, which was where she wanted me to start. Knowing the text of this chapter, I suggested we read from Psalms, or Proverbs, or almost anything other than the fifth chapter of Daniel. But she insisted, so I began. It wasn't long before we reached the part of the chapter I had reservations about, *"Mene mene tekel upharsin."* This translates, "You have been weighed in the balance and found wanting." At that point, Natalie stopped me and said, "That's about me." She seemed to have accepted the fact that she was going to die.

For the next few weeks, I joined with Natalie's children in trying to get her to stop smoking. Though they all complained about it, someone was smuggling cigarettes in to her. Natalie would then slip out on the balcony and light one up. Finally, however, we convinced Natalie to stop smoking. Not long after that, she was transferred to hospice, as it was assumed she had only a little longer to live. There, too, I visited her daily.

On the last day I saw her, I had a friend with me. Natalie said, "Jerry, I'm ready to die. But I have one favor to ask. Will you bring me a cigarette? I want to smoke one last cigarette before I die." I said, "Absolutely not." She replied, "What do you think it will do, kill me?" I wasn't persuaded but she kept insisting. So finally, almost in desperation, I said, "Look, I'll go home and pray about it. And if the good Lord says it's all right, then I'll bring you a cigarette." To a degree, Natalie had developed a spiritual dimension from the discussions we had had during the previous weeks.

She agreed. She told me which brand to buy if God said yes. So I went home, just two blocks away. My friend who was with me was from out of town. He was an editor of one of my books. While I prepared something to eat, he said, "When are you going to ask the Lord about Natalie?" Both he and Natalie had taken my promise to pray seriously, though I had assumed the answer was so obvious it would be a waste of time to even ask.

But a promise is a promise, so I offered a brief prayer. Much to my surprise, the little voice said, "Do it." I was shocked. But once again it demonstrated that we never really know the mind of God and that the only way to find out is to ask. I went to the store and purchased the pack of cigarettes. I then returned to the hospice and gave one to Natalie. I pushed her wheelchair outside and sat and watched her smoke her last cigarette. When she finished it, she died peacefully. Why should I have thought that the nicotine was any worse for her than the morphine being pumped into her veins hourly? It was an important if not surprising lesson in love.

One Friday afternoon, I was paged to the emergency room. They had brought in a man who had just experienced a massive stroke. Four family members were there. It would be an understatement to say they weren't handling it well. They were screaming, crying, bouncing off the walls and off each other, accusing each other of causing the stroke, etc. I could see that this was going to be one of my more challenging duties as a chaplain.

I gathered them together in a room and spoke to them at length. I then ordered something for them to drink and promised I would go to the emergency room and find out their loved one's condition. Before leaving, the wife asked if I would offer a prayer for her husband, which I did. During the prayer, I was prompted to say the man would recover, so that is what I uttered in the prayer.

I went to ER, where physicians had just completed surgery on the man. I didn't have to ask. I knew the outcome from the looks on their faces. But I asked anyway. They assured me the stroke was massive and there was no real hope of recovery. I recall the term "vegetable" being used. That scared me. Knowing how emotionally volatile this family was, and realizing what I had mentioned in my prayer, I was concerned.

I therefore concocted a plan: I would suggest another prayer before I left the family and then set the record straight, mentioning nothing in the second prayer about any recovery from the stroke.

When I visited the family again, I didn't have to suggest another prayer. Much to my relief, they requested it. They said they were so comforted by the first prayer, they wanted me to pray for their husband and father again. During this prayer, however, I was prompted to say the same thing again, thus reassuring the family of his recovery.

This created a conundrum for me. I was certain of the spiritual inspiration I had received. Yet, I also knew what the doctors had said. I therefore decided to go to recovery and see if I could get a more promising opinion of the man's condition from the nurses. Once again, I was assured the man's condition was terminal; it was just a matter of time.

I stayed with the family until they moved their loved one to the intensive care unit. By that time, it was evening and time for me to go home. Before I left, however, the family once again asked me to offer a prayer for the man's recovery. I said to myself, "This is your last chance to put the record straight. Whatever you do, don't say he's going to recover from his stroke." So once again I offered a prayer, and once again I was prompted to make the same promise.

I then left for home, assuming I would return the first day of the week only to discover the man had died. I passed a nervous weekend. I was even more apprehensive as I came to work Monday morning. What would be the condition of this man and his family? I went to the front desk and checked the roster. Sure enough, he was still in intensive care. I went upstairs to see how things were and was greeted by his wife and son. The man was still in a coma.

The wife said, "We are so comforted and reassured by your prayers, would you mind saying another for us?" Once again, the same assurance came out of my mouth. I had no sooner finished the prayer than the man came out of his coma. He sat up in bed, looked at his son, and said, "What are you smiling at, you knucklehead?" I walked out of the room saying to myself, "Oh ye of little faith!"

I would often be asked, "Why this man? Why not others or anyone who has had a massive stroke?" My reply was always the same, "I don't know." The only thing I know is that someone, some force out there, knows the outcomes of these things, and that we can access that information. We can also influence that force and turn it in our direction, if it is right. So when the little voice speaks to you, accept it, have faith in it and act upon it. That's the best answer I have to such a difficult question.

One day, I met a man waiting for out-patient surgery to remove a tumor on his head. He asked if I would pray for him, which I did. The prayer assured him the operation would go smoothly and be a success. And so it was.

A few days later, at his follow-up exam, he dropped in to see me. He told me how much he had appreciated the prayer and how reassuring it had been to him. I asked him to stay in touch, and if any complications developed that I could help with would he please contact me.

Three months later, I received a phone call. He told me he had contracted a staph infection, very likely during the surgery, and by now the infection had become life-threatening. His attending physicians had told him that unless they could find an effective antibiotic, he would probably succumb to the infection within weeks. He had already received one antibiotic through an IV pump. When his liver became affected, it was discovered he was allergic to the antibiotic. This had further weakened him, now making recovery even more unlikely. He was told there were few other antibiotics to choose from for treating such a massive infection.

While in this condition, the man had remembered my offer to help. As I visited him in the hospital, I found him heavily medicated. The infection had settled in his spine and was causing extreme pain. His attending physician was doubtful yet hopeful for his recovery. She told me that even if he survived, a full recovery wasn't possible as there had been extensive damage to his spine.

I then asked the man what he wanted me to do. His answer: "Pray for my recovery, just as you did prior to the surgery." I inquired if he himself had prayed about it and he said he hadn't—he didn't know how to pray. So I struck a deal with him. I said, "I'll do as you ask, but you have to do something for me. I want you to learn to pray and then offer a prayer after I'm finished." He agreed.

I then left him for several minutes and found a place of solitude, where I could get centered and see if I could determine what I should pray for. As usual, the little voice whispered to me. It said, "It is not his time. Bless him that he will recover."

I returned to his room, closed the door, and administered the blessing as indicated by the still small voice, telling him he would make a full recovery. He squeezed my hand and wept. I said, "OK, it's your turn." He then offered the most pure, simple, and humble prayer I have ever heard. Then, I wept. Two months later, he returned to full-time work, having completely recovered.

The power of prayer is indeed profound, and you don't necessarily have to be well schooled in the process for it to be effective. I should hasten to add, however, that sometimes the little voice has indicated to me that a person is *not* going to survive, that it is, in fact, his or her time to go. I don't want to give the impression that prayer can save everyone from every disease or complication. Prayer can't always facilitate a cure, but it can always aid in the healing process.

On my daily rounds, I became friends with an aged man named George, who suffered from an inoperable cancer. I had also become acquainted with his daughter and granddaughter. As an only child, his daughter could do nothing but cry and beg her father not to die and leave her.

After a protracted stay in the hospital, the man was transferred to hospice, where he was heavily medicated for his severe pain. From our conversations it became clear that he was ready to die. But he felt guilty about passing away because his daughter was so distraught about losing her father.

After seeing him suffer from the constant alternation between extreme pain and a drug-induced stupor, I spoke with his granddaughter and explained that George wanted to die but would not do so because his daughter, her mother, kept pleading for him to stay. I asked if it would be OK to speak with her grandfather about "permission to die." Though she was skeptical about the effectiveness of my intervention, she gave her consent and was in favor of letting her grandfather go.

So I met with George, his daughter, and granddaughter together. After a sweet visit, I walked the two women to the exit and returned to the man's bedside. I grasped his hand and said, "George your family loves you, and they know you must pass away, just as you do. If you're ready to die, you now have permission to go." He looked up, beamed at me as if to say, "Thank you," and with a heavy sigh passed away with a smile on his face.

Sometimes, giving a person permission to die—to pass on to the world of departed spirits—is also a true act of love. Not surprisingly, most deaths in hospitals occur in the early morning, when patients are alone, when they won't offend members of the family by dying.

The boss called me one day, wanting my input on a now-daily event involving local schoolchildren. As soon as school was out, a number of boys would stop by the hospital on their way home and head for the kitchens that were located on every floor. We always kept a supply of cups of ice-cream in the refrigerators for use by patients and staff. Somehow, the boys had discovered these. They would visit the kitchens on a regular basis and take off with all or most of the ice-creams. The hospital police had been contacted, as well as myself, to come up with a solution to this annoyance.

There is a saying, "A hammer sees everything as a nail," and that was the case with the police. Their solution was to arrest the boys and make an example of them to the community, thereby sending a message to the rest of the kids who might get similar ideas. Our philosophy at Griffin, however, was to demonstrate love in everything we did.

I therefore asked the police to allow me, as chaplain, to speak with the boys first. During the next several days, I lingered around the kitchens, waiting for the boys to show up. When they did, I stopped them just as they were leaving a kitchen with jackets full of ice-creams. I asked if we could chat. I explained that we didn't mind them taking some of the ice-creams but not so much that there was none left for others. I further suggested that we would like to resolve this matter in a loving way, but that we were prepared to go to the police if necessary. After a little more discussion, they agreed to take no more than one cup of ice-cream per boy per day, leaving plenty for other folks.

As they began to follow this procedure, I would "accidentally" run into the boys and ask how they enjoyed their ice-cream. Soon, we would stop and chat. Within several months of this, the boys began volunteering their service at the hospital, all of which cost us a little love and understanding and a ten-cent cup of ice cream.

LOVE

I tell thee Love is Nature's second sun,

Causing a spring of virtues where he shines;

And as without the sun, the world's great eye,

All colours, beauties, both of Art and Nature,

All beauties bred in women are in vain.

All virtues born in men lie buried,

For love informs them as the sun doth colours,

And as the sun reflecting his warm beams

Against the earth, begets all fruits and flowers;

So love, fair shining in the inward man,

Brings forth in him the honorable fruits

Of valor, wit, virtue, and haughty thoughts,

Brave resolution, and divine discourse.

Oh, 'tis the Paradise, the heaven of earth.

by George Chapman
from All Fooles
circa 1605

12

The person who cannot bear chastening cuts himself
off from the blessings of heaven
—Ophelia Kennedy

A Few Words About Prayer

As a chaplain at Griffin, I was often asked to give suggestions or explanations about the process of prayer—how to get answers, inspiration, and so forth. I will therefore include a few principles that have worked for me, which may also be helpful to you.

People commonly refer to God, or the power of the universe, as our Father in heaven. One reason this title has assumed such common use is that it expresses the way God or this higher power relates to us, which, in turn, parallels the way people relate to each other. Let's examine human relationships first.

There are essentially two kinds of human relationships an adult can have, a parent–child and an adult–adult relationship. Although children begin life within an adult–child relationship, the goal of every parent is that a child should ultimately become independent and enjoy adult–adult relationships.

Translated into a divine–human paradigm, this means that initially, when we attempt to develop a relationship with God or a higher power, such a liaison generally begins with a dependent relationship—with God as parent and us as children. As the relationship progresses, however, God, or the higher power I refer to as God, exerts great efforts to help us mature and become independent. That independent relationship is key to a healthy liaison with God and, in a real sense, with other adults also.

But the idea of such independence sometimes confuses people. After becoming used to God being directly involved in their decisions, progressing to independence as they mature can be a tremendous challenge. However, those who make this transition are vastly different people than those who don't. This doesn't mean that with maturity you forget or abandon God, anymore than you would forget or abandon your parents when you grow up. It simply means that you use our own judgment more in making decisions.

For example, if I were to ask a man to go to my car and retrieve my briefcase, so long as he was headed in the right direction I wouldn't need to communicate with him. Only if he strayed from that direction would I feel a need to give him further guidance. In short, you don't develop someone's independence by directing him at every turn.

Translated into an adult relationship with God, I do the following. I consider all possible options I have regarding an issue. I then prayerfully decide which one I feel best about and proceed to implement it. I change my decision only if the little voice directs me to do so. That way, I am in tune with God—with all the advantages this brings of his divine benevolence—and yet I enjoy a high degree of autonomy.

Of course, this raises the question everyone asks, How do you know when you're being directed to make or alter a decision, or to follow *any* guidance from "on high" for that matter? This is difficult to describe and even harder to master. It took me twenty-one years to learn to communicate properly with my earthly parents and to clearly understand their directives. I'm not surprised, therefore, that it takes me many years to learn to communicate properly with my heavenly Parent.

Everyone, in fact, has to develop his or her own personal relationship with the supreme power. From my experience with people, while a divine–human relationship may vary from person to person, each nonetheless follows a basic pattern. The burden of that relationship falls on us—on how we think and act—as God always does his part.

The underlying principle of divine–human relationships is that God communicates with us through our spirit. When we align our lives with divine truths, and eternal principles, things happen more fluently than when we deviate from them. When our physical or lower appetites direct our behaviors, for example, it is much more difficult for the spirit to receive direction from this supreme and eternal Source.

That is one reason why fasting can be helpful in learning to communicate with the divine power in the universe. By fasting, we force the physical part of us into subjugation to the spirit. This helps our spiritual side be in charge, making us more receptive and opening us up to divine guidance.

Exactly how your higher power communicates with you is an individual thing and can be learned only through practice. However, the process I'm describing shouldn't be confused with intuition, gut feeling, conscience, and so forth, which are different processes than communicating with God. There exists excellent publications and other resources you can consult for further information on this subject.

Another thing I learned while working at Griffin is that you can actually determine your own fate. And if you live your life under divine inspiration, your fate can be favorable indeed. I had once been angry and had lavished hate and vengeance upon my academic superiors. Now, I was working at a job that was exciting and challenging, while at the same time I brought home a bigger paycheck than my former college president. Best of all, I was supremely happy because I was doing what I loved most.

In fact, the reason I was working at Griffin ultimately went back to my being fired as division director at the college. Now, my misery had turned to joy. My job at the hospital was to help others discover happiness and love and to ensure that these principles were embodied in their work. As I walked the hospital halls being pleasant and happy with everyone, I discovered something about myself: I was becoming pleasant and happy.

Because my program at the university was conducted primarily in the evening, I would spend most of the day at Griffin and then afterwards head for the university. As I would come from the hospital—where I was happy, loving, and positive toward all—my attitude automatically spilled over into my college work. Besides teaching classes, I also walked the halls, speaking with everyone in pleasant tones. I thus realized that now I was happy and cheerful in my academic environment as well. The sages and philosophers were right: you become what you think.

Happiness is indeed a learned behavior, as love is. I always knew this intellectually but I had never been required to put it into action. Until I reached that point, it had not moved from my head into my heart nor become an integral part of my being.

When I explained these concepts to others, I would use the following image. Imagine your heart is a cup. In that cup, you place your emotions. Then, after a while the cup becomes full. If you've put hate and anger into the cup, then your heart will be full of hate and anger. Simple enough, right? The question is, how do you get the hate and anger out?

A simple way to eliminate negative emotions is to start pouring love and happiness into the cup. As the cup can only hold so much, when you pour in love something has to come out. In other words, the hate and anger become displaced with love. If you do this consistently enough, love will ultimately replace all negative feelings in your heart.

Important to this process is serving others, which is nearly always an act of love. Thus, we literally *choose* whether or not we'll be happy through our voluntary acts of love. Nowhere is this more apparent than in parents who love and serve their children. After feeding, changing diapers, bathing, cuddling, clothing, reading books, rearing, providing for, teaching, and educating their children, parents naturally love those whom they have served so well.

A young man once came to Stephen Covey and said, "I don't love my wife." Stephen said, "That's easy. Love her, then." The young man said, "You don't understand, I don't love her anymore." Stephen's response was, "Then start loving her again." The young man had bought into Hollywood's version of love.

Here, then, is a word of warning. Counterfeits of love tend not to work in the process of dispelling negative feelings. Only love will force out envy, jealousy, anger, hate, and so forth, every time. Taking advantage of others or violating your inner spiritual compass will handicap your efforts in this regard. So if the anger in your "cup" is not being displaced, take a closer look at what you are accepting as love. There's a good chance it is a counterfeit, not love.

LOVE

Love is the only bow on life's dark cloud.
   It is the Morning and Evening Star.
It shines upon the cradle of the babe,
   and sheds its radiance upon the quiet tomb.
It is the mother of Art,
   inspirer of poet, patriot and philosopher.
It is the air and light of every heart,
   builder of every home,
kindler of every fire of every hearth.
   It is the first to dream of immortality.
It fills the world with melody,
   for Music is the voice of Love.
Love is the magician,
   the enchanter, that changes worthless things to joy,
and makes right royal kings and queens of common clay.
   It is the perfume of the wondrous flower
- the heart – and without that sacred passion,
   that divine swoon,
we are less than beasts:
   but with it earth is heaven and we are immortal.

Robert G. Ingersoll

13

It may make a difference for all eternity whether
we do right or wrong today
—James Freeman Clark

Alternative Health Care

As if spiritualizing Griffin wasn't enough, before I arrived the hospital had begun integrating a variety of complementary health modalities into its medical and convalescent programs. Having taught holistic health in a summer institute for fourteen years, I immediately became involved in these alternative healthcare disciplines.

We adopted yoga in addition to meditation—which John had already started—as part of our new heart disease reversal program. Acupuncture, homeopathy, naturopathy, and hypnosis soon followed. If before this we hadn't given the medical doctors and technical staff sufficient alternative approaches to health to feel concerned about, now we certainly had!

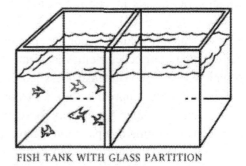

FISH TANK WITH GLASS PARTITION

The first time an alternative-healthcare intern visited us, she gave a slide presentation to the management team and explained to us the basis of naturopathic medicine. Her presentation was well thought out and included slides and other audio-visual material. As I sat listening to her explanations, I said to my-

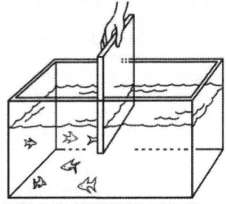

WHEN GLASS PARTITION IS REMOVED, FISH WILL NOT SWIM INTO OTHER SIDE OF THE TANK.

self, "Even a fool can understand this." Wrong! After her presentation, a medical doctor sitting next to me said, "I don't get it." And he didn't. I have since learned why.

Deepak Chopra illustrates this inability to understand another point of view by using a fish tank. You fill a fish tank with water and put a glass divider in the middle, separating the tank into two equal parts. You then put fish in one side of the tank. For the first few days, the fish will swim into the glass divider that prevents access to the opposite side. But after a month, when you remove the glass divider, the fish will never swim to the other side of the tank. They will swim only to where the divider once was and then turn sharply as if they had swum into the glass partition that was once there.

According to Chopra, scientists call this phenomenon, Premature Cognitive Commitment. He says, "Because of our initial sensory experiences, and our interpretation of them, we make a certain commitment to reality, and then that *becomes* our reality."

Once we have been conditioned to believe we can swim on only one side of the tank, our minds are committed to that limitation and we are then generally unable to venture to the opposite side. I had an academic dean who put it this way, "We are all victims of our own perceptions." Indeed, we often seem willing to defend our eccentricities as if our view of reality is the only correct or complete view. Such defensiveness seems especially prevalent among those of us who are most "trapped within our truth."

We couldn't blame the doctors for their one-sided view of medicine. They had been swimming in a partitioned tank for so long, they were unable to go to the other side. Having taught holistic health all those years, I was well aware of the difficulty of getting people to even *peek* into the other side. For example, I experienced difficulties with several local Christian ministers once by quoting Thich Nhat Hanh, a Buddist monk. That was much too far into the other side of the tank for them.

After working at the hospital for a time, it no longer became necessary to start management meetings with a spiritual thought. We now began with meditation or yoga or any variety of modalities that patients were demanding as part of their healthcare. We thought this a good way to expose hospital staff to what patients participated in.

If we hadn't caught national attention before this, now we certainly had. A small community hospital was blazing a trail towards holistic health, showing others how it could be done! I have to admire John for that. He was a man of vision and courage.

Soon, Griffin's personnel, especially John, were being invited to participate in national workshops. More and more, the hospital was taking on a national flavor and setting trends in healthcare. When people asked me, "How do you pull this off?" my response was, "Look at the boss—he's willing to swim in the other side of the tank, and he invites the rest of us to test the water with him."

In retrospect, I now realize we may have been moving too fast for the majority of Griffin's staff. But it was an exciting and innovative time. I would go to work thinking, "What can we create today? How can we improve the system? How can we integrate holistic healing, spirituality, and love into the healthcare system and thus into the lives of people." By the end of the day, we usually had figured out a way.

We often had retreats, at which we would brainstorm for new ideas. No taboos characterized these meetings; we swam freely on both sides of the tank. If you suggested something, it would be treated as a legitimate idea. It would be given due consideration, a worthy discussion, and accorded a decision, yea or nay. John was a master at this. He would listen, question, weigh arguments, and then decide. He was uncanny in his ability to make good final decisions.

Whenever we had those kinds of meetings at the university, the faculty would immediately take refuge in the status quo and play it safe. As creatures of a politically charged academic institution, they feared to leap into the unknown. They were essentially shell-shocked through considerations of self-preservation. So you can imagine the joy I experienced watching this creative process at Griffin, actually witnessing new ideas blossom and become reality daily.

During my second year at the hospital, I had minor surgery. I ended up with post-surgical traumatic stress, very possibly from a combination of medications. I went into a depression and developed phobias that almost immobilized me. I was afraid to ride an elevator, to be alone, to be in a group, wear a necktie, and so forth. That made working in a three-story building difficult.

I walked into John's office one day and explained my dilemma. John put his arms on my shoulders, gave me a hug, and said, "Take as much time as you need to get well. Work at what you can and we'll cover the rest." What a refreshing change that was from the usual institutional response! But this reaction was commonplace from those who worked at Griffin. What a warm and sincerely loving environment this hospital had become!

At the university, my depression would have caused a major disruption. I would have had to fill out a ream of paperwork, obtain medical certificates, provide justifications, and so forth. At the hospital, my word was good enough. I knew there was sincere concern for my well-being and a real sense of love. In fact, it actually appeared to me that at Griffin we had implemented, or were in the process of implementing, a practical course on Love and Health.

Important to remember is that this hospital experiment had started out very tentatively, feeling its way into new territory. Griffin had been an indebted, dysfunctional, and unhealthy enterprise. It was a place that preyed on the public and practiced questionable medicine. Other organizations had wanted to buy it so they could make cosmetic changes, sell it at a profit, and see it trashed.

Just ten years into the experiment and the hospital had been transformed into a loving, healing, and profitable institution. People traveled from all over the world to tour this miracle, this Healthcare Camelot. We entertained visiting groups from hospitals throughout the United States, Canada, Australia, England, Japan, and many other countries.

But after these glorious years, there arose contention in Camelot. Griffin had changed from a unique local experiment into a national phenomenon. Local board members were being replaced by people with impressive medical credentials from other parts of the country. Jealousies between these board members and the administrative cabinet soon became apparent and grew more pronounced by the day. For we who had participated in the hospital's gradual transition into a holistic healing institution, all this occurred in an atmosphere we had assumed was one of love and spirituality. Such an assumption made us unprepared for what happened next.

As tensions built up, one incident touched off a chain reaction. The firing of a vice-president, to which some on the board violently objected, quickly led to a complete division among its members. There followed three months of terrible upheaval. People again wanted to start swimming in the half of the tank they knew best, the one they had been familiar with all their lives. They understood that in order to have their way and gain complete control of the hospital—in other words, to abandon alternative healthcare and return Griffin to being a small community institution, practicing traditional medicine—they had to dispose of the boss.

A tremendous organized effort was therefore made to get rid of John Bustelos. Every day, a new story would appear in the newspapers. Most of these were half truths mixed with distortions and false assertions. Some were even tales of actual failures. But, as William Blake warned, "A truth told with bad intent beats all the lies you can invent."

After months of conflict, John finally resigned as CEO. As you might suspect, those of us who had supported him and his policies received our pink slips in short order.

John's friends and associates then organized a "retirement" party for him. If you attended, you could assume you had already been asked to leave the hospital, or soon would be. For a present, I bought John a watch I had seen him admire in San Francisco when we attended a conference. I also gave him a book on holistic health, which many of us signed. This is what I wrote in the book:

For most of my adult life, I longed to labor where leaders led with love, vision, and integrity. Just once, I wanted to work in an environment that placed people over profit, love over power. I was ready to assume such was not of this world, that we mortals could never attain it. Thanks for proving that it can be done, for allowing me to see, even for one bright moment, that compassion, caring, honesty, empathy, healing, and love can blend together. Other institutions may come and go, but Camelot will be remembered forever.

Your friend and brother,
Jerry

I had thus been a part of the birthing of two unique experiments, a course on Love and Health and the spiritual nativity of a hospital. I had experienced the growing pains of both and seen each blossom into something beautiful. But I had also seen each come to an end, its growth arrested and its beauty fade.

Like Griffin, the course on Love and Health was born, lived a full life, and had a lasting impact on many people. The very year I retired from teaching, the university dropped the course from its Health Education curriculum and abolished it altogether. I was reminded of what Wellington had once said, "When you educate a person and give him no moral direction, you create nothing more than a clever devil."

As for the hospital, it is still there. I'm told it is still a great place to work. It is now a successful community hospital. It no longer attempts to have a national presence but maintains a traditional status quo. A major difference is that King Arthur no longer resides there; and from everything I've heard, it shows.

What have I learned from my labors at these institutions? That being fired is not necessarily a bad thing, that you can convert life's reverses into truly positive experiences. I also learned to love more and deeper than before. I have my former vice-president and nemesis, who is now my friend, to blame for that. Thank you, Bob.

I learned that anger kills and love heals, that if we know how to love, unconditionally, without reservation—to love especially those who have "wronged" us—then health and happiness will surely find us. Love sustains us in our challenges, in our search for truth, in our quest for happiness. Faith affords us the promise that what we search for is attainable. It provides the balm that binds our wounds until at last our hope is realized. To paraphrase Paul, "All things work together for good to those who love..."

The End

Jerry Ainsworth and his associates may be contacted at:
Loveandhealth.org

THE INVITATION

It doesn't interest me what you do for a living,
    I want to know what you ache for
and if you dare to dream of meeting your heart's longing.

I doesn't interest me how old you are,
    I want to know if you will risk looking like a fool
for love, for your dream, for the adventure of being alive.

It doesn't interest me what planets are squaring your moon,
    I want to know if you touched the center of your own sorrow,
if you have been opened by life's betrayals,
    or if you have become shriveled and closed from fear of further pain.

I want to know if you can sit with pain, mine or yours,
    without moving to hide it, or fade it, or fix it.

I want to know if you can be with joy, mine or your own,
    if you can dance with wildness, and let the ecstasy fill you
to the tips of your fingers and toes without cautioning us
    to be careful, to be realistic, to remember the limitations of being human.

It doesn't interest me if the story you are telling me is true,
    I want to know if you can disappoint another to be true to yourself,
if you can bear the accusation of betrayal and not betray your own soul,
    if you can be faithful and therefore trustworthy.

I want to know if you can see Beauty, even when it is not pretty, every day,
    and if you can source your own life from its presence.

I want to know if you can live with failure, yours and mine,
    and still stand on the edge of the lake and shout to the silver of the full moon.

It doesn't interest me to know where you live or how much money you have,
    I want to know if you can get up after a night of grief and despair,
weary and bruised to the bone, to do what needs to be done to feed the children.

It doesn't interest me who you know or how you came to be here,
    I want to know if you will stand in the center of the fire with me and not shrink back.

It doesn't interest me to know where or what or with whom you have studied,
    I want to know what sustains you from the inside when all else falls away.

I want to know if you can be alone with yourself,
    and if you truly like the company you keep in the empty moments.

                                        Oriah Mountain Dreamer, Indian Elder

Acknowledgments

My deepest appreciation goes to all the students who attended my classes on Love and Health. They were a great inspiration and deepened my appreciation of the tremendous impact love has on all our endeavors, including education.

I wish to thank two close friends who helped me immensely with Love and Health. Dr. Douglas Winborn, who assisted in the management of my summer Love and Health Institutes. Also Dr. A. Harris Stone, who was integral to the creation, design and success of the International Love and Health Congress.

Many people encouraged, even pressed me to write this book. My dear friends, York and Nancy Butler, helped me overcome my initial inertia, as did an early student and dear friend, Jim Aulenti. My good friend, Dr. Joel Eisenberg, with his frequent phone calls and boundless love was a constant reminder that this story needed to be written.

I'm deeply indebted to John Bustelos and Jerry Sinnamon, who gave freely of their time, wisdom, and knowledge of those parts that relate to Griffin Health Services.

My good friend, Kevin Webster, kept my computers running even when it meant a dozen frantic calls in a single night.

I also wish to express my gratitude to the congenial staff at the Hotel Calinda Nututun in Palenque, Mexico, where I wrote the original manuscript. My sister, Bibbit Pierce, allowed me to spend countless hours in her home, and gave generously of her time and wisdom, in the formulation of the final manuscript.

A dear friend of many years, Dr. Bernie Siegel, was kind enough to read the manuscript and offer organizational and editorial advice. Bernie, who has admirably translated the concepts he teaches into practice, was always willing to help with my Love and Health classes.

A friend and colleague of many years, Dr. Rod Lane, was kind enough to read, edit and offer substantial suggestions, especially relating to my work place. Doing this at the time he retired and moved into a new house was indeed an act of love. Other editing assistance came from my good friend Avraham Gileadi and a lady with a great mind and spirit, Cathy Marshall.

Lastly I must mention a dear friend of over thirty years, Mr. Irv Leveton. Before he died, Irv provided the sketches for the twelve ingredients mentioned in this book. These concepts reflect the personality of this gentle man, and a more generous, kind, and loving soul I have never met.

APPENDIX

Appendix A

WHAT I HAVE LEARNED – About Love

I've learned –
That you cannot make someone love you. All you can do is be someone who can be loved. The rest is up to them.

I've learned –
That no matter how much you care, some people just don't care back.

I've learned –
That it takes years to build up trust but only seconds to destroy it.

I've learned –
That it's not what you have in your life, but who you have in your life that counts.

I've learned –
That you can get by on charm for about fifteen minutes. After that, you'd better know something.

I've learned –
That you shouldn't compare yourself to the best others can do, but to the best you can do.

I've learned –
That it's not what happens to us that's important. It's how we react to what happens.

I've learned –
That you can do something in an instant that will give you heartache for life.

I've learned –
That no matter how thin you slice it, there are always two sides.

I've learned –
That it's taking me a long time to become the person I want to be.

I've learned –
That it may be easier to react than to plan ahead, but it's much less effective.

I've learned –
That you should always leave loved ones with loving words. It may be the last time you see them.

I've learned –
That you can keep going long after you think you can't.

I've learned –
That we are responsible for what we do, no matter how we feel.

I've learned –
That either you control your attitude or it controls you.

I've learned –
That regardless of how hot and steamy a relationship is at first, passion fades and there had better be something stronger to take its place.

I've learned –
That heroes are the people who do what has to be done when it needs to be done, regardless of the consequences.

I've learned –
That learning to forgive takes practice.

I've learned –
That there are people who love you dearly, but just don't know how to show it.

I've learned –
That money is a lousy way of keeping score.

I've learned –
That sometimes the people you expect to kick you when you're down will be the ones to help you get back up.

I've learned –
That just because someone doesn't love you the way you want them to, doesn't mean they don't love you with all they have.

I've learned –
That maturity has more to do with the experiences you've had and what you've learned from them and less to do with how many birthdays you've celebrated.

I've learned –
That no matter how good a friend is, they're going to hurt you every once in a while and you must forgive them for that.

I've learned –
That it isn't always enough to be forgiven by others. Sometimes you have to forgive yourself.

I've learned –
That no matter how badly your heart is broken, the world doesn't stop for your grief.

I've learned –
That background and circumstances may have influenced who we are, but we are responsible for who we become.

I've learned –
That just because two people argue, it doesn't mean they don't love each other, and just because they don't argue, it doesn't mean they do.

I've learned –
That we don't have to change friends if we understand that friends change.

I've learned –
That your life can be changed in a matter of seconds by people who don't even know you.

I've learned –
That even when you think you have no more to give, when a friend cries out to you, you will find strength to help.

I've learned –
That the paradigm we live in is not all that is offered to us.

I've learned –
That credentials on the wall do not make a decent human being.

Following are Quotes used at the hospital in 1996-97

I've learned –
That a strong code of ethics is as reliable as a compass.

I've learned –
That trust is the single most important factor in both personal and professional relationships.

I've learned –
That enthusiasm is caught, not taught.

I've learned –
That generous people seldom have emotional and mental problems.

I've learned –
That regardless of color or age, we all need about the same amount of love.

I've learned –
That good company is often more healing than words of advice.

I've learned –
That if you care, it shows.

I've learned –
That kindness is more important than perfection.

I've learned –
That nothing is more fun than a job you enjoy.

I've learned –
That it's taking me a long time to become the person I want to be.

I've learned –
That if you look for the worst in life and in people, you'll find it. But if you look for the best, you'll find that instead.

I've learned –
That you shouldn't look back except to learn.

I've learned –
That if you give a pig and a boy everything they want, you'll get a good pig and a bad boy.

I've learned –
That you shouldn't go through life with a catcher's mitt on both hands. You need to be able to throw something back.

I've learned –
That the person with big dreams is more powerful than one with all the facts.

I've learned –
That to experience the wonder of life through the eyes of a child is the most rewarding feeling in the world.

I've learned –
That you learn most from people who are learning themselves.

I've learned –
That there are no unimportant acts of kindness.

I've learned –
That when children want their parents' attention, they will go to extreme lengths to get it.

I've learned –
That I can't change the past, but I can let it go.

I've learned –
That when you have an argument with your spouse, the first one who says, "I'm sorry I hurt your feelings; please forgive me," is the winner.

I've learned –
That although it's hard to admit it, I'm secretly glad my parents are strict with me.

I've learned –
That it takes a lot more creativity to find out what's right than what's wrong.

I've learned –
That you can't expect your children to listen to your advice and ignore your example.

I've learned –
That work enjoyed is as much fun as leisure.

I've learned –
That the more a child feels valued, the better his values will be.

I've learned –
That whenever I decide something with kindness, I usually make the right decision.

I've learned –
That going the extra mile puts you miles ahead of your competition.

I've learned –
That if you depend on others to make you happy, you'll be endlessly disappointed.

I've learned –
That you shouldn't confuse a black crayon with a Tootsie Roll.

I've learned –
That you should wade in a creek every chance you get.

I've learned –
That people are never sneaky in only one area of their life.

I've learned –
That nothing very bad or very good, ever lasts for very long.

I've learned –
That my worst decisions were made when I was angry.

I've learned –
That an economist is the only person who can be right just 10 percent of the time and still get a paycheck.

I've learned –
That if love isn't taught in the home it's difficult to learn it anywhere else.

I've learned –
That people are more influenced by how much I care than by how much I know.

I've learned –
That plotting revenge only allows the people who hurt you to hurt you more.

I've learned –
That most people resist change, and yet it's the only thing that brings progress.

I've learned –
That regrets over yesterday and the fear of tomorrow are twin thieves that rob us of the moment.

I've learned –
That you can tell how good a parent you were by observing your children with their children.

I've learned –
That the faults I have now are exactly the ones my parents tried to correct when I was a child.

I've learned –
That to get the right answer, you have to ask the right question.

I've learned –
That it takes as much time and energy to wish as it does to plan.

I've learned –
That you shouldn't speak unless you can improve on the silence.

I've learned –
That it's never too late to heal an injured relationship.

I've learned –
Never to underestimate the potential and power of the human spirit.

Appendix B

Daily quotes for the hospital, 1994-1998

Our duty as humans is to proceed as if limits on our ability did not exist. We are collaborators in creation.

> Pierre Teilhard de Chardin

The winds and waves are always on the side of the ablest navigators.

> Gibbon

Ability is a poor person's wealth.

> Wren

Always rise from the table with an appetite, and you will never sit down without one.

> Penn

I know well what I am fleeing from but not what I am in search of.

> Michel de Montaigne

Only the shallow really know themselves.

> Oscar Wilde

A man can do more than he thinks he can, but usually less than he thinks he does.

The greatest pleasure in life is doing what people say you cannot do.

> Walter Bagehot

Accuracy of statement is one of the first elements of truth; inaccuracy is a near kin to falsehood.
Tyron Edwards

If a person is worth knowing at all, the person is worth knowing well.
Alexander Smith

The Golden Rule is of no use whatever unless you realize it's your move.
Leo Aikman

Hindsight is an exact science.
Guy Bellamy

It may make a difference for all eternity whether we do right or wrong today.
James Freeman Clark

It is better to wear out than to rust out.
Richard Cumberland

Iron rusts from disuse, stagnant water loses its purity, and in cold weather becomes frozen, even so does inaction sap the vigors of the mind.
Leonardo de Vinci

Unless a decision has degenerated into work, it is not a decision at all, it is an intention.
Peter F. Drucker

Never make an assignment if you don't plan to follow up.
Alvin R. Dyer

Every person over forty is responsible for their face.
Ralph Waldo Emerson

He who is firm and resolute in will, molds the world to him or herself. (do not confuse this with being inflexible and stubborn).
Goethe

Every person feels instinctively that all the beautiful sentiments in the world weigh less than a single lovely action.

James Russell Lowell

Only a mediocre person is always at his best.

Somerset Maugham

The world is divided into people who do things and people who get the credit. Try if you can, to belong to the first class. There's far less competition.

Dwight Morron

If at first you don't succeed, you're running about average. DON'T QUIT.

Lay up your treasures in heaven where there is no depreciation.

To do an evil act is base. To do a good one without incurring danger, is common enough. But it is the part of a good person to do great and noble deeds though the person risks everything in doing them.

Plutarch

To will and not to do when there is opportunity, is in reality not to will; and to love what is good and not to do it, when it is possible, is in reality not to love it.

Swedenborg

Unselfish and noble actions are the most radiant pages in the biography of souls.

David Thomas

Active natures are rarely melancholy. - Active and sadness are incompatible.

Bovee

We're united by our doubts and divided by our convictions.

Peter Ustinov

A fanatic is one who can't change his mind and won't change the subject.

Winston Churchill

It is hard to fight an enemy who has outposts in your head.

Sally Kempton

One out of four people in this country is mentally imbalanced. Think of your three closest friends - and if they seem okay, then you're the one.
> Ann Landers

When a stupid man is doing something he is ashamed of, he always declares that it is his duty.
> George Bernard Shaw

Reality is something you rise above.
> Liza Minnelli

Love your enemy - it'll drive him nuts.

Never lend your car to anyone to whom you have given birth.
> Erma Bombeck

Gossip is when you hear something you like about someone you don't like.
> Earl Wilson

It is better to have less thunder in the mouth and more lightning in the hand.
> Cheyenne Chief

It is trial that proves one thing weak and another strong. A house built on the sand is in fair weather just as good as if built on a rock. A cobweb is as the mightiest cable when there is no strain upon it.
> Henry Ward Beecher

There were nuggets of gold in Moses that would never have been found had he remained in Pharaoh's palace. It took forty years of roughing it to bring them to the surface.
> E.P. Brown

The person who cannot bear chastening cuts himself off from the blessings of Heaven.
> Ophelia Kennedy

Too much sun makes a desert.
> Arabian Proverb

Many people owe the grandeur of their lives to tremendous difficulties.
Charles H. Spurgeon

To bear pain without letting it spoil your happiness is true valor.

Stars may be seen from the bottom of a deep well, when they cannot be discerned from the top of a mountain. So are many things learned in adversity which the prosperous person dreams not of.
Spurgeon

The flower that follows the sun does so even in cloudy days.
Leighton

A noble heart, like the sun, showeth its greatest countenance in its lowest estate.
Sir P. Sidney

He who can take advice is sometimes superior to him who can give it.
Karl von Knebel

Advice is seldom welcome. Those who need it most, like it least.
Johnston

If you would not have affliction visit you twice, listen at once to what it teaches.
James Burgh

Whate'er's begun in anger ends in shame.
Benjamin Franklin

When angry, count four! When very angry, swear.
Mark Twain

Anger: an acid that can do more harm to the vessel in which it is stored than to anything on which it is poured.
Seneca

In a controversy the instant we feel anger, we have already ceased striving for the truth, and have begun striving for ourselves.
Thomas Carlyle

People often make up in wrath what they want in reason.
Alger

Anger is an acorn, hate is the tree.
Ainsworth

No matter how much cats fight, there always seems to be plenty of kittens.
Abraham Lincoln

Money will buy a good dog, but it won't buy the wag of his tail.
Josh Billings

Half of the work that is done in this world is to make things appear what they are not.
E. R. Beadle

Reason should direct, and appetite obey.
Cicero

There are few disputes managed without passion, and yet there is scarce a dispute worth a passion.
Sherlock

The soundest argument will produce no more conviction in an empty head than the most superficial declamation, a feather and a guinea fall with equal velocity in a vacuum.
Colton

I never make the mistake of arguing with people for whose opinions I have no respect.
Edward Gibbon

Silence is one of the hardest things to refute.
Josh Billings

All great art is the expression of man's delight in God's work, not his own.
Ruskin

Study rather to fill your mind than your coffers; knowing that gold and silver were originally mingled with dirt, until avarice or ambition parted them.
Seneca

Though we travel the world over to find the beautiful, we must carry it with us, or we find it not.
Ralph Waldo Emerson

Give us clear vision that we may know where to stand and what to stand for - because unless we stand for something, we shall fall for anything.
Peter Marshal (Senate Chaplain)

Belief consists in accepting the affirmations of the soul. Unbelief in denying them.
Ralph Waldo Emerson

Do not wait for extraordinary circumstances to do good actions: try to use ordinary situations.
Richter

Books are immortal children deifying their sires.
Plato

When it comes to giving, some people stop at nothing.

The real acid test of courage is to be just your honest self when everybody is trying to be like somebody else.
Andrew Jensen

Pain nourishes courage. You can't be brave if you've only had wonderful things happen to you.
Mary Tyler Moore

The opposite of courage in our society is not cowardice...it is conformity.
Earl Nightengale

No one would have ever crossed the ocean if he could have gotten off the ship in a storm.

There is no right way to do a wrong thing.

If absence makes the heart grown fonder, how some people must love the church.

It is easier to suppress the first desire than to satisfy all that follow it.
Benjamin Franklin

Difficulties constitute the best education in this life.
Disraeli

Duty makes us do things well, but love makes us do them beautifully.
Phillips Brooks

The things taught in colleges and schools are not an education, but the means of education.
Ralph Waldo Emerson

If I had the choice of educating a boy or a girl, I would educate the girl. If you educate a boy, you educate one, but if you educate a girl, you educate a generation.
Brigham Young

We should be careful to get out of an experience only the wisdom that is in it - and stop there, lest we be like the cat that sits down on a hot stove-lid. The cat will never sit down on a hot stove-lid again - and that is well; but also the cat will never sit down on a cold one anymore.
Mark Twain

Faith is what makes you feel the comfort of the hearth while you're chopping the wood.
Frank A. Clark

Our doubts are traitors, and make us lose the good we oft might win, by fearing to attempt.
William Shakespeare

When I was a boy of fourteen, my father was so ignorant I could hardly stand to have the old man around. But when I got to be twenty-one, I was astonished

at how much he had learned in seven years.
Mark Twain

I have learned that the head does not hear anything until the heart has listened. And what the heart knows today the head will understand tomorrow.
James Stevens

A learned fool is one who has read everything, and simply remembered it.
Josh Billings

All cruelty springs from weakness.
Seneca

He that cannot forgive others, breaks the bridge over which he must pass himself, for every man hath need to be forgiven.
E. Herbert

Only the brave know how to forgive. It is not in the nature of a coward.
Laurence Sterne

Adversity is the trial of principle. Without it a man hardly knows whether he is honest or not.
Henry Fielding

A people that values its privileges above its principles soon loses both.
Dwight Eisenhower

The natural progress of things is for liberty to yield and government to gain ground.
Thomas Jefferson

Those who profess to favor freedom, and yet depreciate agitation, are men who want rain without thunder and lightning.
Frederick Douglass

I don't like to commit myself about heaven and hell - you see, I have friends in both places.
Mark Twain

Nine-tenths of the people were created so you would want to be with the other tenth.

> Horace Walpole

Prosperity makes friends, adversity tries them.

> Publilius Syrus

It's more blessed to give than to receive - especially kittens.

> Bill Cosby

A great many people think they are thinking when they are merely rearranging their prejudices.

> William James

Real happiness is cheap enough, yet how dearly we pay for its counterfeits.

> Hosea Hallou

There is no way to happiness. Happiness is the way.

> Wayne Dyer

Jealousy, the jaundice of the soul.

> John Dryden

We judge ourselves by what we feel capable of doing, while others judge us by what we have already done.

> Henry Wadsdworth Longfellow

The sword of the law should never fall but on those whose guilt is so apparent as to be pronounced by their friends as well as foes.

> Thomas Jefferson

There is a destiny that makes us brothers; None goes his way alone; All that we send into the lives of others comes back into our own.

> Edwin Markham

The hottest coals of fire ever heaped upon the head of one who has wronged you are the coals of human kindness.

> Sterling W. Sill

Try to put into practice what you already know, and in so doing you will in good time discover the hidden things which you now inquire about.
Henry Van Dyke

What you think when you don't have to think, is a good measure of what you are.
David O. McKay

Knowledge and timber shouldn't be much used till they are seasoned.
Oliver Wendall Holmes

I never learn anything from talking. I only learn things from asking questions.
Lou Holtz

Belief put into action leads to faith. Faith put into action leads to knowledge. Knowledge put into action is intelligence. The glory of God is intelligence.
Ainsworth

Strange how much you've got to know before you know how little you know.
Samuel Johnson

It is better to be old-fashioned and right than to be up-to-date and wrong.
Tiorio

Genius may conceive, but patient labor must consummate.
Horace Mann

Middle Age is that perplexing time of life when we hear two voices calling us, one saying, "Why not?" and the other, "Why bother?"
Sydney Harris

Liberty exists in proportion to wholesome restraint.
Daniel Webster

Liberty is the only thing you cannot have unless you are willing to give it to others.
William White

Sin has many tools, but a lie is the handle which fits them all.
Oliver Wendall Holmes

People are lonely because they build walls instead of bridges.
Joseph Fort Newton

A bell is no bell 'til you ring it. A song is no song 'til you sing it. And love in your heart wasn't put there to stay, Love isn't love 'til you give it away.
Oscar Hammerstein

This is my commandment, That you love one another, as I have loved you.
John 15:12

An unloved child will do more harm to society than untreated sewage.
Mary Fulmer

A lie can travel half way around the world while the truth is putting on its shoes.
Mark Twain

You're never too old to grow up.
Shirley Conran

Learn from the mistakes of others - You can't live long enough to make them all yourself.
Janet Hemming

Man is the only animal that blushes. Or needs to.
Mark Twain

A fool and his money are invited places.
Merit Crossword Puzzles

Never does nature say one thing and wisdom another.
Juvenal

Even if you are on the right track, you will get run over if you just stand there.
Arthur Godfrey

Organizations cannot love, only people can. Love may be expressed through organizations, but never by them.

Jerry L. Ainsworth

QUOTES for the hospital - 1995

Civilization is just a slow process of learning to be kind.
Charles L. Lucas

When change is successful we look back and call it growth.

It is always easier to hate something than it is to understand it.

Today, I will practice giving myself a break when I need it. I will give myself the same consideration I would give any other weary traveler.

You can't go on being a good egg forever. You must either hatch or go rotten.
C.S. Lewis

After prayer and fasting, the practice of literary compositions does most to bridle the lusts of the flesh.
Abbe de Fleury

The lion and the calf shall lie down together but the calf won't get much sleep.
Woody Allen

To love oneself is the beginning of a lifelong romance.
Oscar Wilde

Today, I won't challenge anyone else's behavior unless I'm also willing to be part of the solution.

When I was a boy I was told that anybody could become president; I'm beginning to believe it.
Clarence Darrow

The difference between a rut and a grave is the depth.
Bishop Gerald Burrill

Wit has truth in it; wisecracking is simply calisthenics with words.
Dorothy Parker

Everybody's a pacifist between wars. It's like being a vegetarian between meals.

Colman McCarthy

I hate housework! You make the beds, you do the dishes - and six months later you have to start all over again.

Joan Rivers

I am increasingly less compelled to control the lives of my loved ones. I am relieved to put down a tool that has never worked.

All creation is from conflict, whether with our own mind or with that of others, and the historian who dreams of bloodless victory, wrongs the wounded veteran.

W. B. Yeats

Reality is a staircase going neither up nor down. We don't move, today is today, always is today.

Octavio Paz

I like the dreams of the future better than the history of the past.

Thomas Jefferson

In literature, as in love, we are astonished at what is chosen by others.

Andre Maurois

A poor surgeon hurts one person at a time. A poor teacher hurts 130.

Earnest Boyer

Trust in God - but tie your camel tight.

Persian Proverb

I am responsible for my own perceptions of the world. I accept the fact that the world I see is largely the world I make.

If you think it's hard to meet new people, try picking up the wrong golf ball.

Jack Lemmon

The opposite of talking isn't listening, the opposite of talking is waiting.
Fran Lebowitz

No one can make you feel inferior without your consent.
Eleanor Rosevelt

Regret is an appalling waste of energy; you can't build on it; it's only good for wallowing in.
Katherine Mansfield

As I learn to accept my imperfections, I am better able to accept honesty from others.

Our minds are like crows. They pick up everything that glitters, no matter how uncomfortable our nests get with all that metal in them.
Thomas Merton

Experience: A comb life gives you after you lose your hair.
Judith Stern

Sometime they'll give a war, and nobody will come.
Carl Sandburg

Skepticism is slow suicide.
Ralph Waldo Emerson

Life itself is the proper binge.
Julia Child

Practical people are those who know how to get what they want. Philosophers are those who know what people ought to want. Ideal people are those who know how to get what they ought to want.
Edgar S. Brightman

Today, I choose to focus on the possibilities of life rather than the perils.

Knowledge has to be improved, challenged, and increased constantly or it vanishes.
Peter Drucker

It is in the nature of things that a man cannot really improve himself without in some degree improving other people.
Charles Dickens

You have not converted a person because you have silenced him/her.
John Morley

You cannot logic with a sick mind.
Bumper sticker

Those who do not reach a decision through logic and reason, cannot be logiced and reasoned out of it.
Jerry L. Ainsworth

I have learned silence from the talkative, toleration from the intolerant, and kindness from the unkind.
Kahlil Gibran

The experience of the people around me empowers me to have faith in renewal.

Today, I claim the power that is mine to choose the attitude by which I live.

Trust everyone, but cut the cards.
W.C. Fields

Today, I will examine my decisions to be sure I haven't traded compliance for integrity.

The motto on the first coin ever issued by the United States (the 1787 penny) was, *Mind Your Own Business.*

Cooperation is doing with a smile what you have to do anyway.
Nothing is easier than fault-finding; no talent, no self-denial, no brains, no character are required to set up in the grumbling business.
Robert West

The best way to forget your own problems is to help other people solve theirs.

Mother Whale to her offspring: when you are spouting, you are most likely to be harpooned.

Every person is a damn fool for at least five minutes every day; wisdom consists of not exceeding the limit.
Elbert Hubbard

Horse sense is what keeps horses from betting on what people will do.
Oscar Wilde

Education does not mean teaching people what they do not know. It means teaching them to behave as they do not behave.
John Ruskin

There's no limit to what can be accomplished if it doesn't matter who gets the credit.

An optimist is the person who goes to the window every morning and says, "Good morning, God." The pessimist goes to the window every morning and says, "Good god, morning!"

A civil no is better than a rude yes.

Today, I will not look to anybody else for what I can only find in myself.

Nothing will ever be attempted if all possible objections must be first overcome.
Samuel Johnson

People who are busy rowing seldom rock the boat.

When I am angry at myself I criticize others.
Ed Howe
Act the way you'd like to be and soon you'll be the way you act.
George W. Crane

When people speak ill of you, so live that nobody will believe them.
Plato

The person who trusts others will make fewer mistakes than the person who distrusts them.

Count Cavour

Every man needs a wife. You can't blame everything on the government.

Many times a day I realize how much my own outer and inner life is built upon the labors of my fellowmen, both living and dead, and how earnestly I must exert myself in order to give in return as much as I have received.

Einstein

All your strength is in union. All your danger is in discord.

Longfellow

We promise according to our hopes, and perform according to our fears.

La Rochefoucauld

Today, I will not fake my reactions to anyone or anything. If I don't know how I feel, I will withhold my reaction until I figure it out.

I do not trust those in whom the compulsion to punish is strong.

Nietzsche

Courage is the power to let go of the familiar.

I've never been satisfied with anything we've ever built. I've felt that dissatisfaction is the basis of progress. When we become satisfied in business we become obsolete.

J. Willard Marriott

Today, I am grateful for the healing presence of my friends.

Some ingredients of success: to be able to carry money without spending it; to be able to bear an injustice without retaliating; to be able to keep on the job until it is finished; to be able to do one's duty even when one is not watched; to be able to accept criticism without letting it whip you.

There are two kinds of people: those who want to get things done and those who want to be right.

Archibald Macleish

Nothing is created and perfected at the same moment.

No one ever listened himself out of a job.

Calvin Coolidge

Human nature is something that makes you swear at a pedestrian when you are driving, and at the driver when you are a pedestrian.

Oren Arnold

Never argue with an angry person.

The essence of intelligence is skill in extracting meaning from everyday experience.

Every problem contains within itself the seeds of its own solution.

The person who congratulates self on winning an argument with his/her spouse is a bit premature. The argument isn't over yet.

Happiness is in doing - not having.

I am who I am today. I refuse to be burdened by yesterday's ideas.

The greatest discovery of my generation is that human beings can alter their lives by altering their attitudes of mind.

William James

To err is human. To blame it on the other guy is even more human.

One of the advantages of telling the truth is that you don't have to remember what you said.

He who truly knows has no occasion to shout.

Leonardo

Make it a point to do something every day that you don't want to do. This is the golden rule for acquiring the habit of doing your duty without pain.

Mark Twain

You can make more friends in two months by becoming really interested in other people, than you can in two years by trying to get other people interested in you. Which is just another way of saying that the way to make a friend is to be one.

Dale Carnegie

Today, I will search my conscience for evidence of irresponsibility I may have been filing under other names.

Simplicity of character is the natural result of profound thought.

William Hazlitt

Following the path of least resistance is what makes both rivers and men crooked.

There are only two lasting bequests we can give our children. One is roots, the other wings.

Hodding Carter

If I can make adults of my people, my business will take care of itself. Everything I can do to help them ultimately benefits me.

Henry Ford

Every time history repeats itself the price goes up.

Ability may get you to the top, but only character will keep you there.

We are always the same age inside.

Gertrude Stein

Of all the things you wear, your expression is the most important.

The *Golden Rule* is of no use to you whatever unless you realize that it is your move.

Dr. Frank Crane

You can tell when you're on the right track - it's usually up hill.

The great truths are too important to be new.
Somerset Maugham

The biggest step you can take is the one you take when you meet the other fellow halfway.

The last thing one knows is what to put first.
Pascal

We are not primarily put on this earth to see through one another, but to see one another through.
Peter de Vries

If all our misfortunes were laid in one common heap, whence everyone must take an equal portion, most people would be contented to take their own and depart.
Socrates

Use what talents you possess: the woods would be very silent if no birds sang there except those that sang best.
Henry Van Dyke

The art of being wise is the art of knowing what to overlook.
William James

Nothing is more confusing than the fellow who gives good advice but sets a bad example.

When your work speaks for itself, don't interrupt.
Henry J. Kaiser

Rudeness is a little person's imitation of power.

A diplomatic leader is a person who can tell you to go to hell in such a way that you look forward to the trip.

Be tolerant of those who disagree with you - after all, they have a right to their ridiculous opinions.

Judge people by their questions rather than by their answers.
Voltaire

Imagination is the beginning of creation. You imagine what you desire; you will what you imagine; and at last you create what you will.
George Bernard Shaw

Just about the time most of us finally learn all the answers they change all the questions.

Temper is what gets most of us into trouble. Pride is what keeps us there.

Do you realize that one in every four Americans is unbalanced? Think of your three closest friends. If they seem OK, then you're the one!
Ann Landers

To be trusted is a greater compliment than to be loved.
George MacDonald

It seems to me that people who admit they're wrong get a lot further than people who prove they're right.
Beryl Pfizer

Tact is making a point without making an enemy.

Anger is only one letter short of danger.
Dr. E.D. Hulse

We make a living by what we get - we make a life by what we give.

Most of the things that are really worth knowing cannot be taught.
Coming together is a beginning, keeping together is progress, working together is success.

Our fears are always more numerous than our dangers.
Seneca

QUOTES for the Hospital – 1996

People don't grow old. They merely get old by not growing.

The tragedy of life is not that it ends so soon, but that we wait so long to begin it.

You can take no credit for beauty at sixteen. But if you are beautiful at sixty, it would be your own soul's doing.

There are three requirements necessary to the establishment of resolute enduring character: a faith to live by, a self you can live with, and a purpose to live for.

Personality is what people think we are. Character is what we know we are.

When you want strength, get it out of your heart, not out of your head.

This is the final test of a gentleman – his respect for those who can be of no possible service to him.
                    Phelps -

People show their character in nothing more clearly than by what they think laughable.
Goethe -

No one ever collapsed under the burdens of a single day. It is when the burdens of tomorrow are added to it that it becomes unbearable. Live one day at a time.

Better are the blows of a friend than the false kisses of an enemy.
                    Becket -

I have never been hurt by anything I didn't say.
                    Calvin Coolidge -

Happiness is that particular sensation you acquire when you are too busy to be miserable.

No one has ever injured his eyesight by looking on the bright side of things.

Cooperation is doing with a smile what you have to do anyway.

If you want your neighbor to see what the spirit of Love will do for him, let him see what it has done for you.

Beecher -

There is no outward sign of true courtesy that does not rest on a deep moral foundation.

Goethe -

What do we live for if not to make the world less difficult for each other.

George Elliot -

If you would live your life with ease, do what you ought, not what you please.

Life alone can't give you joy,
   Unless you really will it,
Life only gives you time and space,
   It's up to you to fill it.

The soul would have no rainbows if the eyes had no tears.

The supreme happiness of life is the conviction of being loved for yourself, or more correctly, being loved in spite of yourself.
Victor Hugo -

The soul is dyed the color of one's leisure hours.

Life is fragile - handle with prayer.

What we have done for ourselves alone dies with us. What we have done for others and the world remains and is immortal.

Albert Pipe -

He who does a good turn should never remember it, but he who receives one, should never forget it.

Some of us are trying to serve the Lord without offending the devil.

You are indeed charitable when you give, and while giving, turn your face away so that you may not see the shyness of the receiver.
Kahlil Gibran -

Every person goes down to their grave bearing in their hands only that which they have given away.

Those who bring sunshine to the lives of others, cannot keep it from themselves.
Sir James Barnei

In the final analysis, most of the blessings of life lie in the second mile.

When you meet a person without a smile, give him one of yours.

A smile increases your face value.

We have inherited two ends to use; one to think with, the other to sit on. Heads we win, tails we lose.

A person may fail many times, but he isn't a failure until he begins to blame somebody else.

All men are born equal, but some outgrow it.

Sometimes a noble failure serves the world as faithfully as a distinguished success.

You're on the road to success when you realize that failure is merely a detour.

The trouble with most of us is that we would rather be ruined by praise than saved by criticism.
Norman Vincent Peale

It is something to be able to paint a particular picture, or to carve a statue, and so to make a few objects beautiful; but it is far more glorious to carve and paint the very atmosphere through which we look –to affect the quality of the day

– that is the highest of the arts.
                    Henry Thoreau -

Don't give away your future just to make an hour more stimulating.

Life is interesting only to the interested.

Enthusiasm - the difference between a puddle and a geyser.

Lord, when we are wrong, make us willing to change. And
when we are right, make us easy to live with.
                    Peter Marshall

People are like stained glass windows They glow and sparkle when it is sunny
and bright; but when the sun goes down their true beauty is revealed only if
there is a light from within.

A sound head, an honest heart, and a humble spirit are the three best guides
for mankind.

Our thoughts are blue-prints of what we propose to do.

Courage is fear that has said its prayers.

Living a healthy life is like shaving - no mater how good you do it today you
still have to do it again tomorrow.

Friendship, one soul in two bodies.
                    Pythagoras

Friendship is love without its wings.
                    Byron

An obstacle is something you see when you take your eyes off the goal you are
trying to reach.

Happiness is like jam - you can't spread even a little without getting some on
yourself.

Happiness grows out of harmonious relationships with others, based on attitudes of good will, tolerance, understanding, and love.

Life is a grindstone; whether it grinds you down or polishes you up depends on what you are made of.

Endeavor to so live that when you die even the undertaker will be sorry.
Mark Twain

Strive always to be like a good watch - open faced, with busy hands, pure gold, well regulated, full of good works.

A person's worth is measured by the degree of supervision he requires. The more a person has to be told what to do, checked up and guided, the less he is worth. The employee who burdens his supervisor the most is worth the least.

We make our lives unhappy worrying about the difficulties of our opportunities.

Prayer does not change things - it changes people. People change things.

Practice in life whatever you pray for and it will be given to you abundantly.

He who has no principal draws little interest.

Early to bed, early to rise, until you've learned and earned enough to do otherwise.

No person has ever risen to the real stature of spiritual maturity until they find that it is finer to serve somebody else than it is to serve self.

A smile is a light in the window of the soul, indicating that the heart is at home.

It's too bad that success makes failure out of so many people.

There are no rules for success that work unless you do.

Remember that TRIUMPH is just a little "umph" added to "try."

Nobody cares how much you know until they know how much you care.
Fred Babbel

Pray for a crop, but keep hoeing.

The first mile-stone to being a good citizen is learning how to disagree without being disagreeable.

Courage is not the absence of fear; it is the mastery of it.

Tell me with whom thou art found, and I will tell thee who thou art.
Goethe

Intelligence without wisdom is like a locomotive without a train to pull.

Spirituality can't be bought: it must be absorbed.

Man will never reach his destiny until he realizes there is as much dignity in tilling the soil as there is in writing a poem.
Booker T. Washington

If you are right, take the humble side - you will help the other fellow. If you are wrong, take the humble side - and you will help yourself.

An ounce of practice is worth a pound of preaching.

We have been so anxious to give our children what we didn't have that we have neglected to give them what we did have.

I am persuaded that he who is capable of being a bitter enemy does not possess the necessary virtues that constitute a true friend.

Until you can say no to the unimportant, you can't say yes to the important.

Joy is not in things, it is in us.
Richard Wagner

Your body cannot sprout an ulcer and laugh at the same time.

Three may keep a secret, if two of them are dead.

Apology is often a good way to have the last word.

He who slings mud, loses ground.

Life is 10% what you make it and 90% how you take it.

Everything has its beauty but not everyone sees it.
Confucius

Forbidden fruit is responsible for many bad jams.

We can do anything we want to do if we stick to it long enough.
Helen Keller

Worry is like a rocking horse; it will keep you going but it gets you nowhere.

Anger is frequently more hurtful to us than the injury that provokes it.

When a child is placed in front of a computer and a television set, the computer always wins.
Ron Hansen

It is one thing to itch for something and another to scratch for it.

We have too many people who live without working, and we have altogether too many who work without living.
Charles R. Brown

All that is necessary for the triumph of evil is for good people to do nothing.
Edmund Burke

The capacity to love is primarily determined in our childhood.

QUOTES for the hospital - 1997

Whoever in the darkness lighteth another with a lamp lighteth himself also.
- Auerbach

Strength and struggle travel together.
- Parlette

The hard is the good.
- Goethe

If you want to make life easy, make it hard.
- Shakespeare

Self-reverence, self-knowledge, self control; these three lead to sovereign power.
- Tennyson

He becomes a stout enemy who overcomes his own anger.
- Aristotle

He that ruleth his spirit is greater than he that taketh a city.
- Solomon

Contentment is natural wealth; luxury, artificial poverty.
- Socrates

Howe'er it be it seems to me
  Tis only noble to be good;
Kind hearts are more than coronets,
  and simple faith than Norman blood.
- Tennyson

Temperance and labor are the two best physicians of man; labor sharpens the appetite and temperance prevents from indulging to excess.
- Rousseau

The best preacher is the heart, the best teacher is time, the best book is the world, and the best friend is God.
- The Talmud

We lose the peace of years when we hunt after the rapture of moments.
- Bulwer Lytton

He has achieved success who has lived well, laughed often and loved much; who has gained the respect of intelligent men and the love of little children; who has filled his niche and accomplished his task; who has left the world better than he found it, whether by an improved poppy, a perfect poem, or a rescued soul; who has never lacked appreciation of earth's beauties, nor failed to express it; who has always looked for the best in others and given the best he has; whose life is an inspiration, whose memory, a benediction.
- Robert Lewis Stevenson

From quiet homes and first beginnings,
    Out to the undiscovered ends;
There's nothing worth the wear of winning,
    But laughter and the love of friends.

The person with an educated soul will outlive the person with an educated brain.

It is best not to tell all you know; you may have to respond to an encore.

Follow the river and you will get to the sea.
- Gaelic saying

I will inhibit the expression of pride, envy and malice.
    I will seek self-mastery rather than power over others.
I will turn to the up-look when the outlook is not good.
    I will cultivate the courage that can stand alone.
I will be content to plant seeds rather than blossoms.
    I will keep a "bird in the bush" not made of gold.
I will judge myself severely, others leniently.
    I will listen widely, think deeply and speak discreetly.
I will cultivate the enviable power of forgetting and forgiving.
    I will avoid the practice of looking for easy things.

I will prefer the love and confidence of my own household
   to the praises and plaudits of the multitude.
 I will cultivate the companionship of the
   "Still Small Voice."

In each and all lie the opportunities of an archangel; as the majestic oak lies enfolded in the acorn.

                - Lydia Maria Child

Out of the lowest depth there is a path to the loftiest height.

                - Thomas Carlyle

The error of the ages -
Why so many do not win -
Is always seeking power without,
Instead of power within.

                - Alvin Curtis Shaw

If a man expects and believes great things of himself, it makes no odds where you put him.

                - Thoreau

If I can stop one heart from breaking,
   I shall not live in vain;
If I can ease one life the aching,
   Or cool one pain,
Or help one fainting robin
   Unto his nest again
I shall not live in vain.

                - Emily Dickinson

No man is an island;
No man stands alone.
Each man's joy is a joy to me;
Each man's grief is my own.

We need one another,
So I will defend
Each man as my brother;

Each man as my friend.

I saw the people gather,
I heard the music start.
The song that they were singing
Is still ringing in my heart.

No man is an island;
No man stands alone.
Each man's joy is a joy to me;
Each man's grief is my own.

We need one another,
So I will defend
Each man as my brother;
Each man as my friend.

 - John Donne

God hath not promised
 Skies always blue,
Flower-strewn pathways
 All our lives through;
God hath not promised
 Sun without rain,
Joy without sorrow,
 Peace without pain.

But God hath promised
 Strength for the day,
Rest for the labor,
 Light for the way,
Grace for the trials,
 Help from above,
Unfailing sympathy,
 Undying love.

 - Annie Johnson Flint

Love and smoke are two things which can't be concealed.
 - French Proverb

When you educate a person, and give them no moral direction, you create nothing more than a clever devil.

- Wellington

Do all the good you can,
By all the means you can,
In all the ways you can,
In all the places you can,
At all the times you can,
To all the people you can,
As long as ever you can.

- John Wesley

The greatest pleasure I know is to do a good action by stealth and have it found out by accident.

- Charles Lamb

All who joy would win must share it: happiness was born a twin.

- Lord Byron

Keep your face to the sunshine and you cannot see the shadow.

- Helen Keller

Neuroticisms are more contagious than measles.

- Menninger

There is a destiny that makes us brothers;
 None goes his way alone;
All that we send into the lives of others
 Comes back into our own.

- Edwin Markham

Life is too short for words that hurt;
 For subtle thrusts and for phrases curt;
For motives unkind and for sharp retort -
 For any of these, life is too short.

- Lucile Veneklasen

If you can sit at set of sun

And count the deeds that you have done
  And counting find
One self-denying act, one word
That eased the heart of him that heard -
  One glance most kind,
Which fell like sunshine where he went,
Then you may count that day well spent.
                              - Robert Browning

To mourn a mischief that is past and gone
Is the best way to bring a fresh mischief on.
                              - William Shakespeare

Words are the children of Earth, but deeds are the children of Heaven.
                              - Samuel Johnson

A smooth sea never made a skillful mariner.
                              - Anonymous

Shadow owes its birth to light.
                              - Gray

Adversity is the diamond dust heaven polishes its jewels with.
                              - Leighton

Gold is tried by fire, people by adversity.
                              - Seneca

Hardening of the heart ages people more quickly than hardening of the arteries.

To be seventy years young is sometimes far more cheerful and hopeful than to be forty years old.
                              - Oliver Wendell Holmes

Anger is never without a reason, but seldom a good one.
                              - Benjamin Franklin

When people are wrong and won't admit it, they always get angry.
- Haliburton

Beauty is the highest form of genius, because it needs no explanation.
- Oscar Wilde

You cannot run away from a weakness; you must at some point fight it out, and either win or perish; and if that be so, why not now and where you stand?
- Robert Lewis Stevenson

Faith on a full stomach may be simply contentment. But if you have it when you're hungry, it's genuine.

Doing an injury puts you below your enemy; revenging one makes you but even with him; forgiving it sets you above him.
- Benjamin Franklin

Never does the human soul appear so strong and noble as when it foregoes revenge and dares to forgive an injury.
- Chapin

An injury can grieve us only when remembered. The noblest revenge therefore is to forget.

Virtuous energies are the essential constituents of happiness.
- Aristotle

The measure of a happy person is the ability to be tough with self, and tender with others.
- David P. McKay

Happiness is a man who can enjoy the scenery when he has to take a detour.

To thine own self be true, and good will follow as surely as night does the day. Thou canst not then be false to any man.
- Shakespeare

There are no crown-bearers in heaven that were not cross-bearers here below.
- Spurgeon

My life is my message.

- Ghandi

We may give without loving, but we cannot love without giving.

Those who love deeply never grow old; they may die of old age, but they die young.

Appendix C

BIBLIOGRAPHY

Achterberg, Jeanne G. and Frank Lawlis. *Imagery and Disease.* Champaign, Illinois: Institute for Personality & Ability Testing, 1978.

Ardinger, Barbara. *Seeing Solutions.* New York: Ballantine Books, 1988.

Atwater, P. M. H. *Coming Back to Life.* New York: Ballantine Books, 1988.

Berkowitz, Bernard, et. al. *How to be Your Own Best Friend.* New York: Ballantine Books, 1971.

Borysenko, Joan. *Fire in the Soul: A New Psychology of Spiritual Optimism.* New York: Warner Books, 1993.

Bradshaw, John. *The Family.* Deerfield Beach, Florida: Health Communications Inc., 1988.

Bradshaw, John. *Healing the Shame that Binds You.* Deerfield Beach, Florida: Health Communications Inc., 1988.

Braheny, Mary and Diane Halperin. *Mind, Body, and Spirit.* Deerfield Beach, Florida: Health Communications, Inc., 1989.

Buscaglia, Leo. *Personhood.* New York: Ballantine Books, 1978.

Colton, Helen. *Touch Therapy.* New York: Kensington Publishing, 1983.

Cousins, Norman. *Anatomy of an Illness.* New York: Bantam Books, 1979.

Cousins, Norman. *Head First.* New York: Penguin, 1989.

Cousins, Norman. *The Healing Heart.* New York: Avon Books, 1983.

Covey, Stephen. *Spiritual Roots of Human Relations.* Salt Lake City, Utah: Desert Book Company, 1970.

Covey, Stephen. *The 7 Habits of Highly Effective People.* New York: Summit, 1991.

Crosby, John. *Illusion and Disillusion.* Belmont, California: Wadsworth Publishing Company, 1973.

Curran, Dolores. *Traits of a Healthy Family.* Minnesota: Winston Press, 1983.

Fast, Julius. *Body Language.* New York: Pocket Books, 1970.

Ferguson, Marilyn. *The Aquarian Conspiracy.* Boston: Houghton Mifflin Company, 1980.

Fromm, Eric. *The Art of Loving.* New York: Harper and Row, 1956.

Furth, Gregg. *The Secret World of Drawings.* Boston: Sigo Press, 1988.

Garrison, Judith and Scott Shepard. *Cancer & Hope.* Minnesota: Compcare, 1989.

Hayes, Jody. *Smart Love.* Los Angeles: Jeremy P. Tarcher, Inc., 1989.

Houe, Herbert. *Do Not Go Gentle.* New York: Norton, 1981.

Jaffe, Dennis. *Healing from Within.* New York: Simon and Schuster, 1980.

Jampolsky, Gerald and Diane Cirincione. *Love is the Answer.* New York: Bantam, 1990.

Jampolsky, Gerald. *Love is Letting Go of Fear.* New York: Bantam Books, 1970.

Jampolsky, Gerald. *Teach Only Love.* New York: Bantam Books, 1983.

Justice, Blair. *Who Gets Sick.* Los Angeles: Jeremy P. Tarcher, Inc., 1987.

Kabat-Zinn, Jon. *Wherever You Go, There You Are.* New York: Hyperion, 1994.

Keating, Kathleen. *Hug Therapy (Volumes 1 and 2).* Minnesota: Compcare Publishers, 1983.

Keyes, Ken. *The Power of Unconditional Love.* Coos Bay, Oregon: Loveline Books, 1990.

Krieger, Dolores. *The Therapeutic Touch.* Englewood Cliffs, New Jersey: Prentice Hall, 1979.

Larsen Earnest. *Love is a Hunger.* Minnesota: Compcare Publishers, 1979.

Levin, Lowell, et. al. *Medicine on Trial.* New York: Prentice Hall, 1988.

Locke, Steven and Douglas Colligan. *The Healer Within.* New York: E. P. Dutton, 1986.

Lynch, James. *The Broken Heart: The Medical Consequences of Loneliness.* New York: Basic Books, Inc., 1979.

Lynch, James. *The Language of the Heart.* New York: Basic Books, Inc., 1989.

MaCrae, Janet. *Therapeutic Touch.* New York: Knopf, 1988.

May, Rollo. *Love and Will.* New York: Delta Books, 1969.

Mandel, Robert. *Open Heart Therapy.* Berkeley, California: Celestial Arts, 1984.

Mandel, Robert. *The Miracle is You.* North Haven, Connecticut: Cinsu Publishing, 1983.

Montagu, Ashley. *Touching.* New York: Harper and Row, 1978.

Moore, Nancy and Henrietta Komras. *Patient-Focused Healing.* San Francisco: Jossey-Bass Publishers, 1993.

Myss, Caroline. *Anatomy of the Spirit.* New York: Harmony Books, 1996.

Myss, Caroline. *Why People Don't Heal and How They Can.* New York: Harmony Books, 1997.

Ornish, Dean. *Love & Survival.* New York: Harper Perennial, 1998.

Outka, Gene. *Agape: An Ethical Analysis.* New Haven, Connecticut: Yale University Press, 1972.

Paddison, Sara. *The Hidden Power of the Heart.* Boulder Creek, California: Planetary Press, 1995.

Padus, Emrika. *The Complete Guide to Emotions and Your Health.* Emmaus, Pennsylvania: Rodale Press, 1986.

Paul, Jordan and Margaret. *From Conflict to Caring.* Minnesota: Compcare, 1989.

Pearsall, Paul. *The Heart's Code.* New York: Broadway Books, 1998.

Pelletier, Kenneth. *Mind as Healer, Mind as Slayer.* New York: Delta Books, 1977.

Porterfield, Kay. *Violent Voices.* Deerfield Beach, Florida: Health Communications, Inc., 1989.

Powell, John. *Unconditional Love.* Allen, Texas: Argus Communications, 1978.

Siegel, Bernie. *How to Live Between Office Visits.* New York: Harper Collins Publishers, Inc., 1993.

Siegel, Bernie. *Love, Medicine and Miracles.* New York: Harper and Row, 1986.

Siegel, Bernie. *Peace, Love and Healing.* New York: Harper and Row, 1989.

Simmermacher, Donald. *Self Image Modification.* Deerfield Beach, Florida: Health Communications, Inc., 1989.

Sinatra, Stephen. *Heartbreak & Heart Disease.* New Canaan, Connecticut: Keats Publishing, Inc., 1996.

Small, Jacquelyn. *Becoming Naturally Therapeutic.* Austin, Texas: Eupsychian Press, 1981.

Weil, Andrew. *Spontaneous Healing.* New York: Fawcett Columbine, 1995.

Weiner, Michael. *Maximum Immunity.* Boston: Houghton Mifflin Company, 1986.

Welwood, John. *Challenges of the Heart.* Boston: Shambhala Publications, 1985.

Williams, Redford and Virginia. *Anger Kills.* New York: Penguin, 1984.

Zaleski, Philip and Paul Kaufman. *Gifts of the Spirit.* San Francisco: Harper Collins Publishers, 1997.

CPSIA information can be obtained
at www.ICGtesting.com
Printed in the USA
LVOW03s2024060617

537170LV00002B/2/P